J. Ferrini-Mundy
1991

D1292143

J. Ferrini-Mundy
1991

The Language of Functions and Graphs

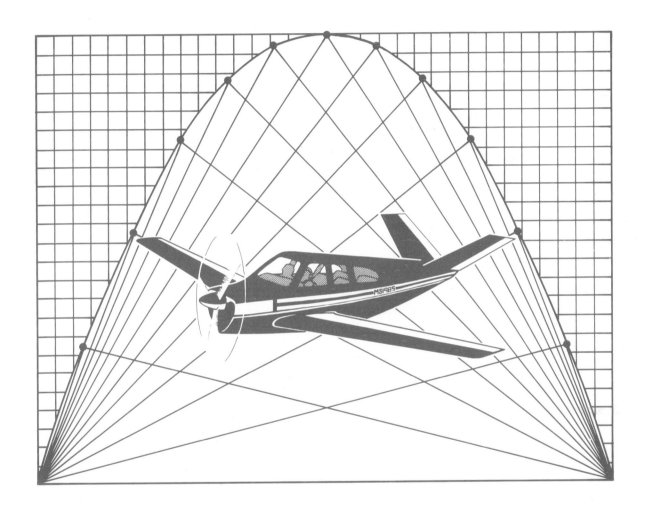

An Examination Module for Secondary Schools

Joint Matriculation Board
Shell Centre for Mathematical Education

AUTHORS AND ACKNOWLEDGEMENTS

This Module has been produced by the joint efforts of many teachers working with the Shell Centre for Mathematical Education and the Joint Matriculation Board. It was developed as part of the Testing Strategic Skills programme which aims gradually to promote a balanced range of curriculum activities through the development of new examination questions.

The Module is based on classroom research and teaching materials by:

Malcolm Swan

with help from Alan Bell, Hugh Burkhardt and Claude Janvier.

It was produced by the Shell Centre team:

> Alan Bell, Barbara Binns, Gard Brekke, Hugh Burkhardt, Rita Crust, Rosemary Fraser, John Gillespie, Kevin Mansell, Richard Phillips, Andy Pierson, Jim Ridgway, Malcolm Swan and Clare Trott,

co-ordinated by Clare Trott, and directed by Hugh Burkhardt.

Specific responsibility for the three sections of the book was as follows:

Specimen Examination Questions:	John Pitts
Classroom Materials:	Malcolm Swan
Support Materials:	Rosemary Fraser

This material has been developed and tested with teachers and pupils in over 30 schools, to all of whom we are indebted, with structured classroom observation by the Shell Centre team. These teachers include:

> Paul Bray, Paul Davison, Tansy Hardy, Anne Haworth, David Kaye, Steve Maddern, John Mills, Geoff Orme, John Rose, Chris Smith, Nick Steen, Aileen Stevens, Jon Stratford, Glenda Taylor and Alan Tizard.

We gratefully acknowledge the help we have received from:

* Paul Morby and the University of Birmingham Television and Film Unit in the making of the video material.

* The ITMA collaboration at the Shell Centre and the College of St. Mark and St. John in the development of the microcomputer programs.

* Peter Wilson and his colleagues at the Joint Matriculation Board, together with the staff of Richard Bates Ltd, in the preparation of this Module.

* Sheila Dwyer and Jenny Payne for much typing and even more patient support.

* Douglas Barnes, Trevor Kerry, David Fielker and Clive Sutton in granting us permission to reproduce extracts from their books.

* John Doyle (Automobile Association), Alan Heywood (Ffestiniog Railway), and Geraldine Mansell (Consumer's Association) in allowing us to reproduce data from their publications.

This book was designed, edited and illustrated by Malcolm Swan.

The Language of Functions and Graphs

CONTENTS

An expanded version of the contents follows on the next page . . .

EXPANDED CONTENTS

Each of these questions is accompanied by a full marking scheme, illustrated with sample scripts.

Unit A

This unit involves sketching and interpreting graphs arising from situations which are presented verbally or pictorially. No algebraic knowledge is required. Emphasis is laid on the interpretation of global graphical features, such as maxima, minima, intervals and gradients. This Unit will occupy about two weeks and it contains a full set of worksheets and teaching notes.

Unit B

In this Unit, emphasis is laid on the process of searching for patterns within realistic situations, identifying functional relationships and expressing these in verbal, graphical and algebraic terms. Full teaching notes and solutions are provided. This Unit again occupies approximately two weeks.

A Problem Collection

This collection supplements the material presented in Units A and B.
It is divided into two sections. The first contains nine challenging problems
accompanied by separate selections of hints which may be supplied to pupils
in difficulty. The second section contains a number of shorter situations
which provide more straighforward practice at interpreting data.
This material provides a useful resource which may be dipped into from time
to time as is felt appropriate. Solutions have only been provided for the nine
problems.

Support Materials

These materials are divided into two parts—those that are part of this book,
and those that accompany the videotape and microcomputer programs in the
rest of the pack. They offer support to individual or groups of teachers who
are exploring the ideas contained in this module for the first time.

Classroom Discussion Checklist

INTRODUCTION TO THE MODULE

This module aims to develop the performance of children in interpreting and using information presented in a variety of familiar mathematical and non-mathematical forms. Many pupils are well acquainted with graphs, tables of numbers, and algebraic expressions and can manipulate them reasonably accurately—but remain quite unable to interpret the global features of the information contained within them. In addition, many pupils are rarely given the opportunity to use mathematical representations autonomously rather than imitatively, to describe situations of interest.

Mathematics is a powerful language for describing and analysing many aspects of our economic, physical and social environment. Like any language, it involves learning new symbolic notations, and new 'grammatical rules' by which these symbols may be manipulated. Unfortunately, in mathematics, it is possible to learn these rules without understanding the underlying concepts to which they refer, and this often results in mathematics becoming a formal, dull, and virtually unusable subject. When learning any foreign language, pupils are indeed asked to learn a certain amount of grammar, but they are also given opportunities to express themselves using the language, both orally and through 'free' writing. In a similar way, it is often helpful to set aside the mechanical, grammatical side of mathematical language and spend a few lessons where the emphasis is on *using* mathematics as a *means of communication*. Using mathematics in this way requires a wider range of skills than have usually been taught or tested in public examinations, and a greater mastery and fluency in some of those techniques that are already included. This module has been developed to meet some of these needs.

The Cockcroft Report* emphasises the need for such skills in many of its recommendations. It also recognises that in order to achieve these aims, a wider range of classroom activity and of teaching style is necessary.

Two important instances are in paragraphs 34 and 243:
> "Most important of all is the need to have sufficient confidence to make effective use of whatever mathematical skill and understanding is possessed, whether this be little or much."

> "Mathematics teaching at all levels should include opportunities for:
> * exposition by the teacher;
> * discussion between teacher and pupils and between pupils themselves;
> * appropriate practical work;
> * consolidation and practice of fundamental skills and routines;
> * problem solving, including the application of mathematics to everyday situations;
> * investigational work."

---

*Mathematics Counts, HMSO 1982.

In this module, the emphasis is therefore on:

— helping pupils to develop a fluency in using the mathematical language of graphs, tables and algebra in order to describe and analyse situations from the real world.

— creating a classroom environment which encourages thoughtful discussion as pupils try to comprehend or communicate information presented in a mathematical form.

This presents most teachers with some classroom activities that are relatively unfamiliar. The teaching materials have been designed, and carefully developed in representative classrooms, to guide and to help the teacher in exploring these new demands in a straightforward and gradual way. The Support Materials explore more reflectively what is involved—with the video showing various teachers in action and raising issues for discussion. The microcomputer is there to provide its own powerful support during the absorption of these classroom skills and in other teaching.

The list of knowledge and abilities to be tested in the Board's O-level examination include the abilities to understand and translate information between different mathematical and non-mathematical forms, to interpret mathematical results, and to select and apply appropriate techniques to problems in unfamiliar or novel situations.

The importance of these skills is also underlined by their prominence in the National Criteria for the General Certificate of Secondary Education. Any GCSE scheme of assessment must test the ability of candidates to:

3.1 recall, apply and interpret mathematical knowledge in the context of everyday situations;

3.3 organise, interpret and present information accurately in written, tabular, graphical and diagrammatic forms;

3.7 estimate, approximate and work to degrees of accuracy appropriate to the context;

3.10 interpret, transform and make appropriate use of mathematical statements expressed in words or symbols;

3.14 make logical deductions from given mathematical data;

3.15 respond to a problem relating to a relatively unstructured situation by translating it into an appropriately structured form;

3.16 respond orally to questions about mathematics, discuss mathematical ideas and carry out mental calculations.

The level of performance to be expected in most of these areas is described in the Criteria only in general terms, without even the limited specific illustrations provided for traditional content areas. This reflects the general lack of experience in existing examinations in assessing such skills. This module illustrates how they may be examined and how teachers may prepare pupils for such questions—the research and development effort has gone into ensuring that all the elements work well with pupils and teachers representative of those who take the Board's examinations. In view of the coming of the GCSE, many of the materials (Unit A in particular) have been designed to be suitable also for pupils of average ability; somewhat different examination tasks will be needed in this context, and suitable questions are being developed and tested.

Specimen
Examination
Questions

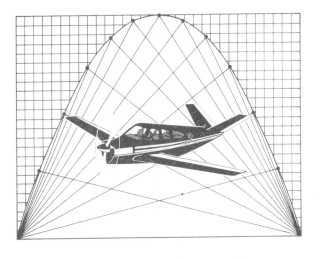

Specimen Examination Questions

CONTENTS

INTRODUCTION

These specimen questions indicate the range of questions that is likely to be asked. The questions actually set may be expected to differ from those given here to about the same extent as they differ from each other.

The marking schemes are designed to give credit for the effective display of some of the following skills:

1. Interpreting mathematical representations* using words or pictures.

2. Translating words or pictures into mathematical representations.

3. Translating between mathematical representations.

4. Describing functional relationships using words or pictures.

5. Combining information presented in various ways, and drawing inferences where appropriate.

6. Using mathematical representations to solve problems arising from realistic situations.

7. Describing or explaining the methods used and the results obtained.

The sample answers which follow the questions are intended to illustrate various aspects of the marking scheme. The number of marks awarded for each question varies according to its length but, as a guideline, a question worth 15 marks should occupy about 20 minutes of examination time.

---

*By 'mathematical representations' we mean information presented graphically, algebraically, or in tabular form.

THE JOURNEY

The map and the graph below describe a car journey from Nottingham to Crawley using the M1 and M23 motorways.

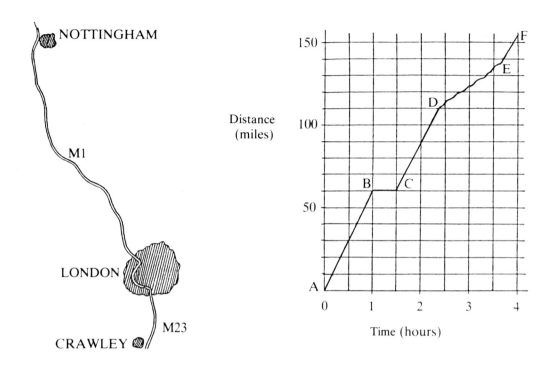

NOTTINGHAM

M1

LONDON

M23

CRAWLEY

Distance (miles)

Time (hours)

(i) Describe each stage of the journey, making use of the graph *and* the map. In particular describe and explain what is happening from A to B; B to C; C to D; D to E and E to F.

(ii) Using the information given above, sketch a graph to show how the speed of the car varies during the journey.

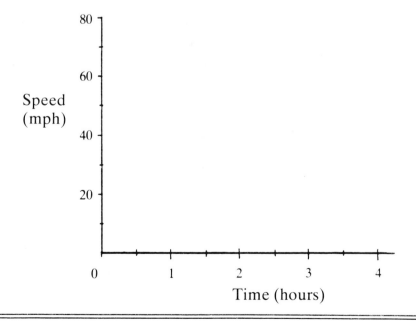

Speed (mph)

Time (hours)

12

THE JOURNEY . . . MARKING SCHEME

(i)   Interpreting mathematical representations using words and combining information to draw inferences.

Journey from A to B	'Travelling on the M1'	1 mark
	'Travelling at 60 mph' (± 5 mph) or 'Travels 60 miles in one hour'	1 mark
Journey from B to C	'Stops' or 'At a service station' or 'In a traffic jam' or equivalent	1 mark
Journey from C to D	'Travelling on the motorway'	1 mark
	'Travelling at the same speed as before' or 'Travelling at 60 mph (± 5 mph) or 'Travels 50 miles in 50 minutes' (± 5 mins.)	1 mark
Journey from D to E	'Travelling through London'	1 mark
	'Speed fluctuates', or equivalent. eg: 'there are lots of traffic lights'. Do not accept 'car slows down'.	1 mark
Journey from E to F	'Travelling on the motorway' or 'Travelling from London to Crawley'.	1 mark

(ii)   Translating into and between mathematical representations.

For the general shape of the graph award:

1 mark	if the first section of the graph shows a speed of 60 mph (± 10 mph) reducing to 0 mph.
1 mark	if the final section of the graph shows that the speed increases to 60 mph (± 10 mph) then decreases to 20 mph (± 10 mph) and then increases again.

For more detailed aspects, award:

1 mark	if the speed for section AB is shown as 60 mph and the speed for section CD is shown as 60 mph (± 5 mph).
1 mark	if the changes in speed at 1 hour and 1½ hours are represented by (near) vertical lines.
1 mark	if the stop is correctly represented from 1 hour to 1½ hours.
1 mark	if the speed through London is shown as anything from 20 mph to 26 mph or is shown as fluctuating.
1 mark	if the graph is correct in all other respects.

A total of 15 marks are available for this question.

Jayne

A →B = You go a long way in a short time
because you are on the m1
B→C = You have stopped for half an hour
for your lunch.
C→D = You travel the rest of the m1 till you
get to London.
D→E= You slow down as you go through London.
E→F = You speed up again on the m23 till
you get to Crawley.

Sarah

A to B → In the first hour, the car
travelled 60 miles. (speed of 60 mph).

B to C → Then between 1 hour and 1½
hours, the car remained stationary.

C to D → Between 1½ hours and 2⅓ hours
at it's original pace of 60 mph.

D to E → Then between 2⅓ hours and 3⅔
hour the car travelled approx 28 miles
at verying speeds

E to F → Then between 3⅔ and 4 hours
the car travelled at approx
50 mph.

Philip

The car starts off from Crawley along the m23 gradually speeding
up and then continuing to London (B) at a constant speed of 60mph.
Between B to C, the car is stationary for half an hour and then
~~then~~ starts on its journey from C to D after 1 and a half hours
from starting, it now travels at a constant speed of 60 mph
for 50 minutes until reaching D. where it slows down to a speed
of 20 mph and then from E to Nottingham, it again speeds up
doing a constant speed for ¼ of an hour when it slows
down as it reaches Nottingham.

Jayne's description depends almost entirely on the map. She does not specify the speed of the car at any stage (although the stop is included). She therefore did not gain the related marks for sections AB, CD and DE. She was awarded 5 marks out of the possible 8.

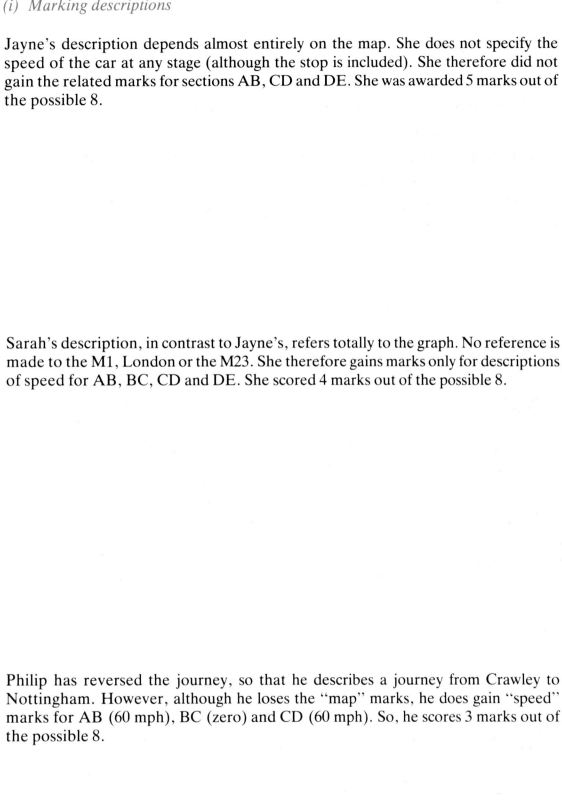

Sarah's description, in contrast to Jayne's, refers totally to the graph. No reference is made to the M1, London or the M23. She therefore gains marks only for descriptions of speed for AB, BC, CD and DE. She scored 4 marks out of the possible 8.

Philip has reversed the journey, so that he describes a journey from Crawley to Nottingham. However, although he loses the "map" marks, he does gain "speed" marks for AB (60 mph), BC (zero) and CD (60 mph). So, he scores 3 marks out of the possible 8.

Angela

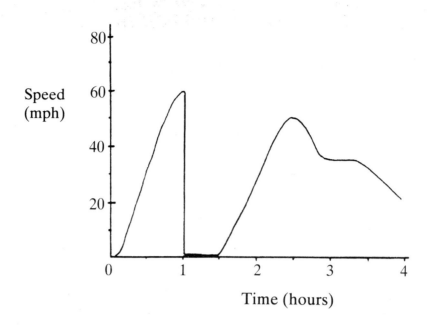

Theresa

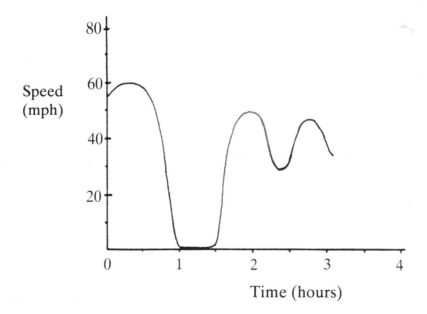

(ii) Marking descriptions

General shape

Angela has shown a decrease in speed in the first part of her graph from 60 mph to 0 mph. However, in the second part of the graph, although the speed increases and then decreases, it does not increase again. Angela was therefore awarded one of the two possible marks here.

Theresa's graph gains both "shape" marks. It decreases from 60 mph to 0 mph, and then correctly increases, decreases and increases again. However, when the graph is marked in detail, she was awarded only one mark (for correctly representing the stop) out of the possible 5.

Robert

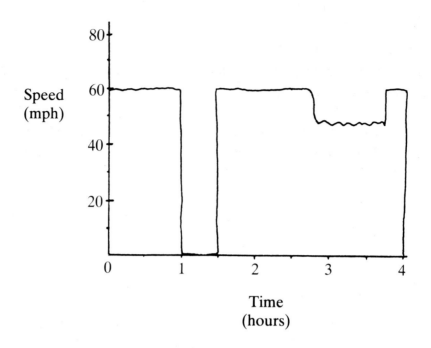

Michael

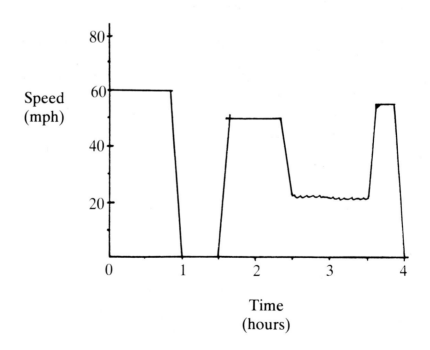

Robert's graph was awarded 3 marks out of the possible 5 for detail. These were given for

*   AB and CD shown as 60 mph.
*   Near vertical lines at 1 and 1½ hours.
*   The stop shown correctly.

Robert did not obtain the final mark as there was one other error not already penalised—the section CD should be represented from 1½ to under 2½ hours, Robert has shown it to be from 1½ to 2¾ hours.

Michael's graph was awarded 4 marks out of the possible 5 for detail. Three were given for

*   The stop shown correctly.
*   Near vertical lines at 1 and 1½ hours.
*   The journey through London shown correctly.

Michael was awarded the fourth mark for having no errors other than those already penalised.

CAMPING

On their arrival at a campsite, a group of campers are given a piece of string 50 metres long and four flag poles with which they have to mark out a rectangular boundary for their tent.

They decide to pitch their tent next to a river as shown below. This means that the string has to be used for only three sides of the boundary.

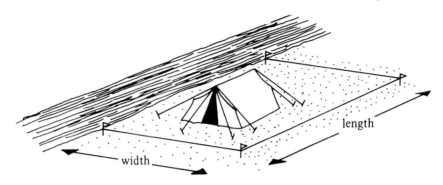

(i) If they decide to make the width of the boundary 20 metres, what will the length of the boundary be?

(ii) Describe in words, as fully as possible, how the length of the boundary changes as the width increases through all possible values. (Consider both small and large values of the width.)

(iii) Find the area enclosed by the boundary for a width of 20 metres and for some other different widths.

(iv) Draw a *sketch* graph to show how the area enclosed changes as the width of the boundary increases through all possible values. (Consider both small and large values of the width.)

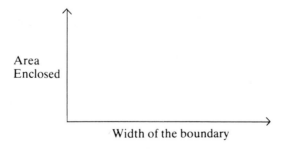

The campers are interested in finding out what the length and the width of the boundary should be to obtain the greatest possible area.

(v) Describe, in words, a method by which you could find this length and width.

(vi) Use the method you have described in part (v) to find this length and width.

CAMPING . . . MARKING SCHEME

(i) and (ii) Describing a functional relationship using words.

(i)	*1 mark*	for length = 10m.

(ii) *3 marks* for 'As the width increases from 0 to 25m, the length decreases linearly (uniformly) from 50m to 0m'.

or for 'As the width increases, the length decreases at twice the rate'.

Part marks: Give 2 marks for 'As the width increases the length decreases linearly (uniformly)'

or 2 marks for 'As the width increases from 0m to 25m, the length decreases from 50m to 0m'

or 1 mark for 'As the width increases, the length decreases'.

(iii) and (iv) Translating information into a mathematical representation.

(iii) *1 mark* for area = 200m^2.

2 marks for finding correct areas for three other widths.

Part mark: 1 mark for finding correct areas for two other widths.

(iv) *2 marks* for a sketch graph which shows a continuous curve with a single maximum point.

Part mark: Give 1 mark for a sketch graph which is wholly or partly straight or consists of discrete points, but shows that the area increases and then decreases.

(v) Describing the method to be used in solving a problem.

3 marks for a clear and complete description of how to find both dimensions.

Part mark: Give 2 marks for a clear and complete description of how to find only one of the dimensions.

Give 1 mark if the explanation is not clear but apparently correct.

(vi) Using mathematical representations to solve a problem.

2 marks for 'width = 12.5m for maximum area'.

Part mark: Give 1 mark for a width given in the interval 12m < width < 13m.

or 1 mark for 'width could be 12m or 13m'.

1 mark for 'length = 25m for maximum area'.
(follow through an incorrect width in the interval 12m ⩽ width ⩽ 13m).

A total of 15 marks are available for this question.

Julian

ii) If the width is increased then the length would get shorter. ie. If the width of each side is increased by 1 metre then the length would be 2 metres shorter.

If the width is decreased by one metre then the length of the boundary would an extra two metres.

Steven

(ii) Starting at the smallest that the width can be, the length will be very long. As the width gets larger then the length must get smaller.

i.e.

	WIDTH	LENGTH	
Small	1m	48m	Great
	10m	30m	
	15m	20m	
Great	24m	2m	Small

Debbie

(ii) as the width increases, the length would get shorter as there is only 50m of string, so the longer the width gets, the shorter the length.

Julian's description was awarded the full 3 marks. He has correctly described the relationship, including the fact that the length decreases at twice the rate at which the width increases.

Steven, by showing values of 1m and 24m for the width, has demonstrated the relationship numerically. He was therefore awarded 2 marks. (He clearly did not consider 0m to be a realistic dimension.)

Debbie has simply stated that as the width increases the length decreases. For this she was only awarded one mark.

Catherine

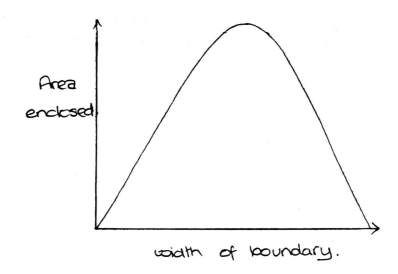

width of boundary.

Andrew

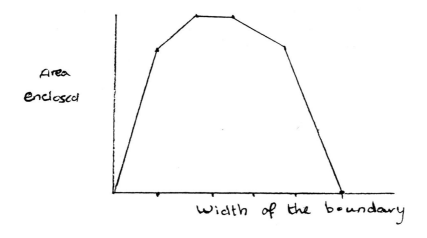

Width of the boundary

Emma

(v) To find this length and width I would look on my graph to find the highest point and follow it down to find the width. Then I would × 2 and − from 50.

Katherine

(v) · Draw a graph as in q.(iv) and find the highest point. Look down and you have the width. It is then easy to work out the length

24

(iv)   Marking sketch graphs

Catherine's sketch clearly shows a single maximum point, while Andrew's sketch is made up of several straight lines, although showing the area to increase then decrease.

Catherine was therefore awarded both marks for her sketch graph while Andrew was awarded one mark.

(v)   Marking descriptions

Emma's answer to part (v) clearly describes the method she will use to find *both* the width and the length corresponding to the maximum area. She was awarded the full 3 marks.

Katherine's answer, however, only describes a method for finding the width. She was therefore only awarded 2 marks out of the possible 3.

Karen

$$W = 12 \qquad A = 26$$
$$L = 26 \qquad \underline{\times 12}$$
$$260$$
$$\underset{1}{52}$$
$$\underline{}$$
$$312 \, m^2$$

$$W = 13 \qquad A = 24$$
$$L = 24 \qquad \underline{\times 13}$$
$$A = 312 \, m^2 \qquad 240$$
$$\underline{72}$$
$$312$$

These are the same.

Karen has calculated the area obtained for widths of 12m and 13m, and has given both in her answer to part (vi). For this she was awarded 1 mark and she also scored 1 mark for correctly giving the corresponding lengths. Karen was therefore awarded a total of 2 marks out of the possible 3 for the numerical answers.

GOING TO SCHOOL

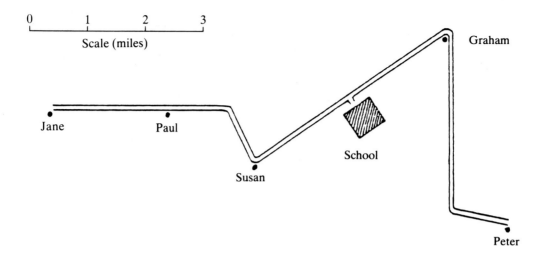

Jane, Graham, Susan, Paul and Peter all travel to school along the same country road every morning. Peter goes in his dad's car, Jane cycles and Susan walks. The other two children vary how they travel from day to day. The map above shows where each person lives.

The following graph describes each pupil's journey to school last Monday.

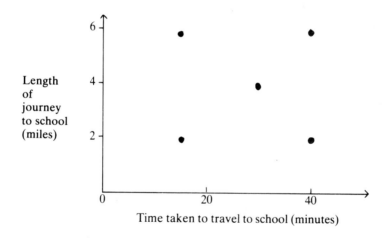

i) Label each point on the graph with the name of the person it represents.

ii) How did Paul and Graham travel to school on Monday? _____

_____

iii) Describe how you arrived at your answer to part (ii) _____

_____

_____

(continued)

28

iv)   Peter's father is able to drive at 30 mph on the straight sections of the road, but he has to slow down for the corners. *Sketch* a graph on the axes below to show how the car's speed varies along the route.

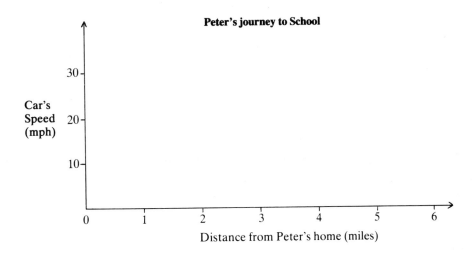

GOING TO SCHOOL...MARKING SCHEME.

(i)   Combining information presented pictorially and verbally, and translating into a mathematical representation.

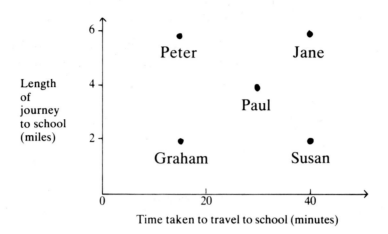

1 mark   if Paul is correctly placed.

1 mark   if Peter and Jane are shown at 6 miles.

1 mark   if Graham and Susan are shown at 2 miles.

1 mark   if Peter and Jane are correctly placed
            or if Graham and Susan are correctly placed.

1 mark   if the diagram is completely correct.

(ii)   Combining information presented in various ways and drawing inferences.

If Part (i) is correct, then award

2 marks   for 'Paul and Graham cycled' or 'ran' (or used a method faster than walking but slower than a car).

Part mark: 1 mark for 'Paul cycled' (or 'ran' etc)
             or 'Graham cycled' (or 'ran' etc)
             or 'Paul and Graham used the same method.'

If Part (i) is incorrect, then award

2 marks   if the answers given for *both* Paul and Graham are consistent with the candidates' diagrams, otherwise give no marks.

30

(iii)   **Explaining the methods used in part (ii)**

> *2 marks*   if the description of the argument used in part (ii) is clear and complete.
> (This description must involve speed, or distance *and* time.)
>
> > Part mark: 1 mark for a description which is not quite complete.
> >
> > or for a description which is not quite clear but apparently correct, or for any description which mentions speed.

(iv)   **Translating information from a pictorial to a graphical representation.**

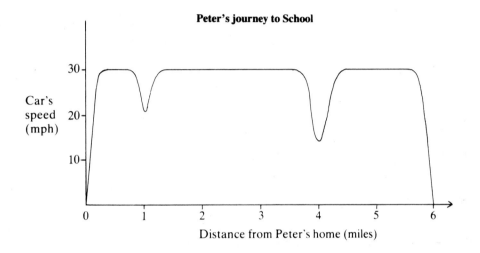

> *1 mark*   if the graph starts at (0,0) and/or finished at (6,0)
>
> *1 mark*   if the graph has two minima to correspond to the two bends
>
> *1 mark*   if the second minimum point is not higher than 25 mph but is lower than the first minimum point
>
> *1 mark*   if the distance between the minima is correct (representing 3 miles approximately)
>
> *1 mark*   if the speed is shown as 30 mph for at least 1 mile in the middle section and between 0 and 30 mph (inclusive) elsewhere
>
> *1 mark*   if the graph is correct in all other respects

A total of 15 marks are available for this question.

Kelly

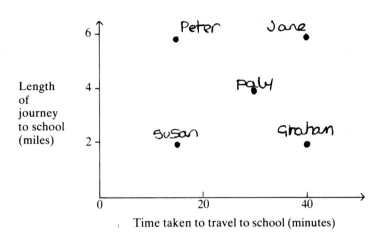

Paul and Graham both cycled to school

Leigh

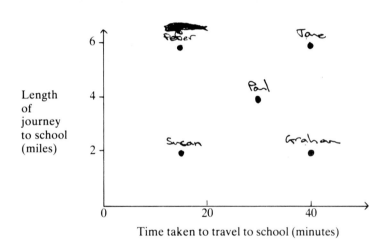

ii Paul and Graham walked to school

Jason

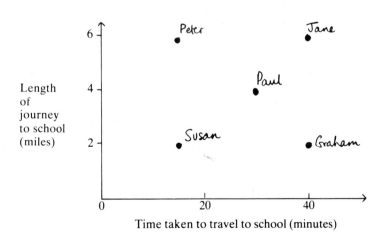

Paul biked it Graham walked

32

Kelly's answer to part (ii) looks as though it is correct but it does not correspond to *her* answer to part (i), so she does not obtain any marks for the answer to part (ii). For part (i) she was awarded 4 marks.

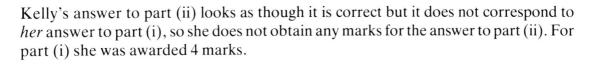

Leigh was awarded 4 marks for his answer to part (i). Paul was correctly placed on Leigh's diagram and therefore the correct deduction would be that Paul did not walk to school. Graham, on the other hand, was placed in such a way that the correct deduction would be that he did walk to school. However, the answers given in part (ii) for *both* Paul *and* Graham need to be correct for the marks to be awarded.

Jason was awarded 4 marks for his answer to part (i). In part (ii) the answers for both Paul and Graham correctly reflect the answer given to part (i). Full marks were therefore awarded for part (ii).

Jackie

If Graham had walked to school he would have taken

as long as Susan

if he had gone in the car he would have beaten Peter

so he must have cycled.

If Paul had walked he would have taken longer than

Susan if he had gone in the car he would

have ~~taken~~ been much quicker than Peter who had

further to go

Steven

3   I arrived at the answer to number 2 because
Jane Paul and Graham are all on a line and
their miles and time go up steadily. Jane went by
like so the other two must have as well.

34

(iii)   Marking descriptions

It is interesting to compare Steven's answer with Jackie's. Jackie has given a "wordy" description, comparing each boy's journey with the other pupils'. Steven on the other hand, has noted the fact that the points corresponding to Jane, Paul and Graham all lie on a straight line and so they must have used the same method of transport. However, both descriptions are clear and correct and were awarded the full 2 marks.

Joanne

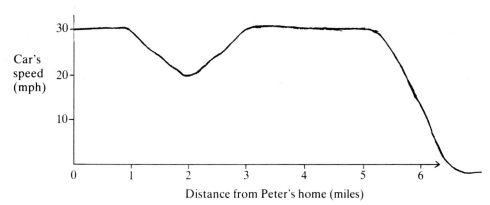

Jane

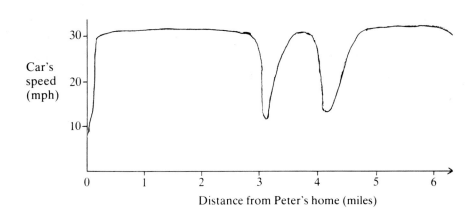

Stephen

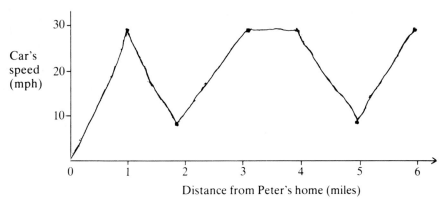

Jason

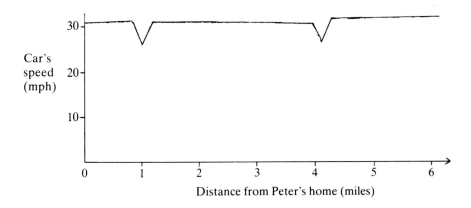

(iv)   Marking sketch graphs

Joanne has only shown one bend on her graph. However, one mark was awarded for representing the straight section correctly at 30 mph for at least one mile. The final mark was not awarded since the bend shown took 2 miles to negotiate—a further error. She obtained a total of 1 mark out of the 6 for part (iv).

Jane was awarded 1 mark out of 5 for the specific points relating to the graph (she represented the two bends as two minima). She was also awarded the final mark because all the errors she made relate to the specific points mentioned in the mark scheme and consequently have already been penalised. So, Jane obtained a total of 2 marks out of 6.

Stephen was awarded 3 marks out of 5 for the specific points relating to the graph (showing 2 bends as 2 minima; these being 3 miles apart; and the middle section being 30 mph for at least 1 mile). However, since Stephen has represented the car as slowing down for 1 mile in approaching the bends and taking another mile to reach 30 mph again, he was not awarded the final mark. Stephen therefore scored 3 marks out of 6.

Jason was similarly awarded 3 marks out of 5 for the specific points relating to the graph. But whereas Stephen did not obtain the final mark, Jason did. If Jason had shown the graph from (0,0) to (6,0) and the second bend more severe than the first, the graph would have been correct. He therefore scored 4 marks out of 6.

THE VENDING MACHINE

A factory cafeteria contains a vending machine which sells drinks.
On a typical day:

* the machine starts half full.

* no drinks are sold before 9 am or after 5 pm.

* drinks are sold at a slow rate throughout the day, except during the morning and lunch breaks (10.30-11 am and 1-2 pm) when there is greater demand.

* the machine is filled up just before the lunch break. (It takes about 10 minutes to fill).

Sketch a graph to show how the number of drinks in the machine might vary from 8 am to 6 pm.

Number of
drinks
in the machine

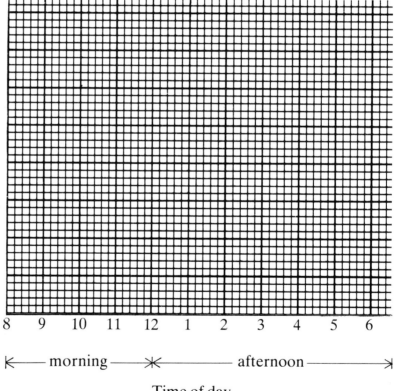

Time of day

38

THE VENDING MACHINE...MARKING SCHEME

Translating words into a mathematical representation.

1 mark   if the graph is horizontal from 8 am to 9 am *and* from 5 pm to 6 pm.

1 mark   if the gradient of the graph ≤ 0 from 9 am to 12 noon.
(Do not accept a zero gradient throughout the period.)

1 mark   if the filling of the machine is represented at some time between 12 noon and 1 pm, and this filling takes not more than 24 minutes (ie, 2 small 'squares' on the graph paper).

1 mark   if the peak of the graph is shown at twice the height of the starting point.

1 mark   if the graph is noticeably steeper from 10.30 am to 11 am and from 1 pm to 2 pm than elsewhere.

1 mark   if the gradient of the graph ≤ 0 from 1 pm to 5 pm.
(Do not accept a zero gradient throughout the period.)

1 mark   if the graph is correct in all other respects.

A total of 7 marks are available for this question

Kevin

Number of
drinks
in the machine

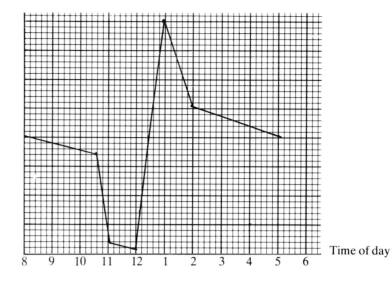

Time of day

Paul

Number of
drinks
in the machine

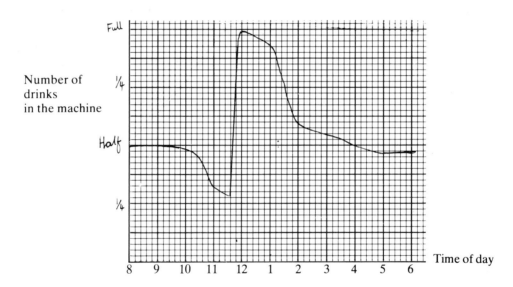

Time of day

Cheryl

Number of
drinks
in the machine

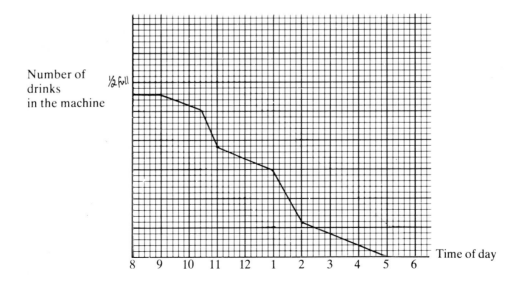

Time of day

40

In Kevin's graph the machine starts dispensing drinks from 8 am so that the representation from 8 am to 9 am is not correct and this mark was lost. He also shows that the machine takes 1 hour to fill and, since this is greater than the permitted 24 minutes given in the mark scheme, another mark was lost. These are the only two errors and so Kevin was awarded 5 out of the possible 7 marks.

In Paul's graph the machine was filled at 11.35 am, which was considered *not* to be "just before lunch" and so he lost one mark here. He has, however, clearly shown a steeper gradient between 10.30 and 11.00 am and also between 1 pm and 2 pm. He has successfully dealt with the period between 12 noon and 1 pm. He was therefore awarded a total of 6 marks.

Cheryl completely ignored the filling of the machine. She has, however, shown a negative gradient between 9 am and 12 noon and from 2 pm to 5 pm, and also clearly shown the slope to be steeper in the appropriate sections. It should also be noted that on a "typical day" the machine would not finish empty. Cheryl was awarded 3 marks out of the possible 7.

THE HURDLES RACE

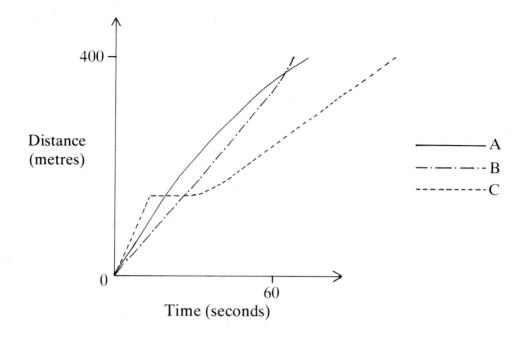

The rough sketch graph shown above describes what happens when 3 athletes A, B and C enter a 400 metres hurdles race.

Imagine that you are the race commentator. Describe what is happening as carefully as you can. You do not need to measure anything accurately.

THE HURDLES RACE... MARKING SCHEME

Interpreting a mathematical representation using words.

1 mark   for 'C takes the lead'

1 mark   for 'C stops running'

1 mark   for 'B overtakes A'

1 mark   for 'B wins'

2 marks   for any four of the following:

        A and B pass C

        C starts running again

        C runs at a slower pace

        A slows down (or B speeds up)

        A finishes 2nd (or C finishes last)

        Part mark: 1 mark if any two (or three) of the above points are mentioned.

2 marks   for a lively commentary which mentions hurdles.

        Part mark: 1 mark for a lively commentary which does not mention hurdles, or for a 'report' which mentions hurdles.

A total of 8 marks are available for this question.

Martin

And they were off. C increased speed very rapidly for the first 150 m and covered a big distance in a very short time. B took it calmly and paced himself to his limits he went reasonably fast and A went faster than B but slower than C at the start, but then C stopped for a rest and carried on slowly coming in last A went faster and kept going, but was overtaken by B who beat A and came first, B won, A was second, and C was third.

Stephen

Here at the start of the race the three athletes are ready to start. There off. Athlete C takes an early lead, Athlete A is close in second and athlete B is in the rear after a bad start. There're approaching the 100m mark. Its still C leading from B A and B is catching up Oh no, C as fell. He's getting up and chasing A and B. At half way A ~~to get ahead~~ has a small lead but B is gradually catching him and it looks like C hasn't much chance of winning. There now in the final 100m A and B are neck and neck, C has just passed halfway. Athlete A crosses the line first B is only just behind him. C is about 100m out. I think C might have won if he didn't fall.

Wendy

Athlete A came 2nd - He started off fairly fast and got slightly slower during the race.

Athlete B came 1st - He started off at a steady rate and picked up speed all the way through the race.

Athlete C came 3rd - He started off going fast, then he fell over and didn't run for a few seconds, then he started running again, gradually getting slower and slower

Martin has mentioned all of the first 4 factors and also 3 of the additional ones. For this he scored 5 marks. Martin's commentary reads more like a report than a commentary, and since he does not mention the hurdles, he was not awarded any "commentary" marks. Therefore, Martin obtained a total of 5 marks out of the possible 8.

Stephen has only mentioned 2 of the first 4 factors and 2 of the additional ones, thus scoring 3 marks. However, Stephen's commentary is lively and interesting although he has ignored the fact that it is a hurdles race. He was awarded one "commentary" mark, making a total of 4 out of the possible 8.

Wendy has also mentioned 2 of the first 4 points, as well as 3 of the additional ones. She was awarded 3 marks for these. Wendy does not, however, obtain any "commentary" marks, since she has described each athlete's run separately, rather than giving a commentary on the race as a whole.

THE CASSETTE TAPE

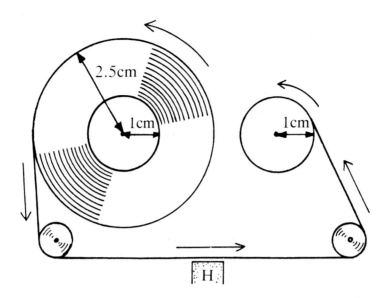

This diagram represents a cassette recorder just as it is beginning to play a tape. The tape passes the "head" (Labelled H) at a constant speed and the tape is wound from the left hand spool on to the right hand spool.

At the beginning, the radius of the tape on the left hand spool is 2.5 cm. The tape lasts 45 minutes.

(i) Sketch a graph to show how the *length* of the tape on the left hand spool changes with time.

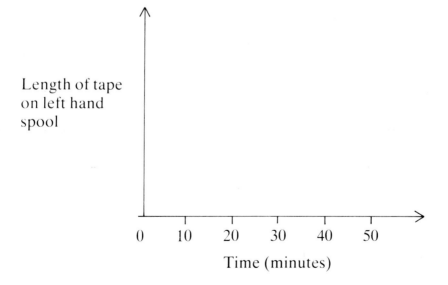

(continued)

46

(ii)   Sketch a graph to show how the *radius* of the tape on the left hand spool changes with time.

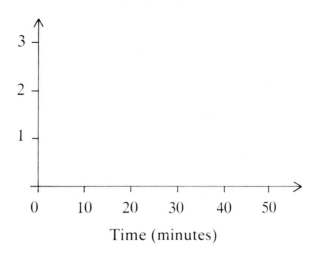

Radius of tape on left hand spool (cm)

Time (minutes)

(iii)   Describe and explain how the radius of the tape on the *right-hand* spool changes with time.

_____

_____

_____

_____

_____

_____

_____

_____

THE CASSETTE TAPE . . . MARKING SCHEME

(i) and (ii)   Translating words and pictures into mathematical representations.

   (i)   *1 mark*   for a sketch graph showing a straight line with a negative gradient.

         1 mark   for a sketch ending at (45,0).

   (ii) *1 mark*   for a sketch beginning at (0,2.5) and ending at (45,1).

         1 mark   for a sketch showing a curve.

         1 mark   for a curve that is concave downwards.

(iii)   Describing and explaining a functional relationship using words.

   2 marks   for a correct, complete description.
   eg: 'the radius increases quickly at first, but then slows down'.

   Part mark: Give 1 mark for 'the radius increases'.

   2 marks   for a correct, complete explanation.
   eg: "the tape goes at a constant speed, but the circumference is increasing" or "the bigger the radius, the more tape is needed to wrap around it".

   Part mark: Give 1 mark for an explanation that is apparently correct but not very clear.

A total of 9 marks are available for this question.

(ii)   Marking sketch graphs

Stephanie

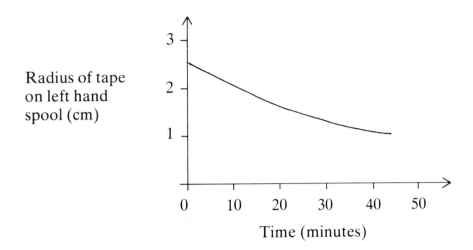

Stephanie's sketch shows a curve beginning at (0,2.5) and ending at (45,1). However, since it is not "concave downwards", she was awarded 2 marks out of the possible 3.

Mark

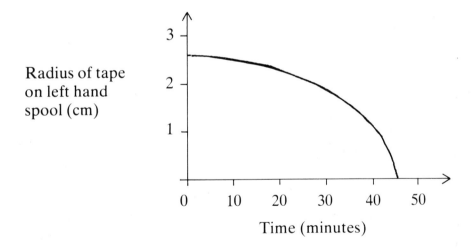

Mark's sketch is a "concave downwards" curve, but does not end at (45,1). He was also awarded 2 marks for this section.

Paul

The radius of tape on the right hand spool
will ~~be~~ grow fast at first and then it will start
to slow down as the radius gets bigger because the speed
of the tape is constant.

Julie

The radius of the tape becomes more on the
right hand side. At first the radius become more
at a high speed because the tape goes quicker
around the spool. The radius is forever increasing
although it is doing this slower and slower because
the tape is getting larger around the spool

Brian

At the start it will have a radius of 0. As the
circumference is getting larger the amount of tape
needed to go round it increases and as the tape
is going past the head at a constant speed the
radius will increase at a high speed at first
but gradually slow down.

50

(iii)   Marking descriptions and explanations

The descriptions and explanations of how the radius on the right hand spool changes with time are often inseparable in the candidates' answers. To illustrate this, and also to demonstrate the range of acceptable responses, 3 scripts are shown—all of which were awarded the full 4 marks for part (iii).

FILLING A SWIMMING POOL

(i) A rectangular swimming pool is being filled using a hosepipe which delivers water at a constant rate. A cross section of the pool is shown below.

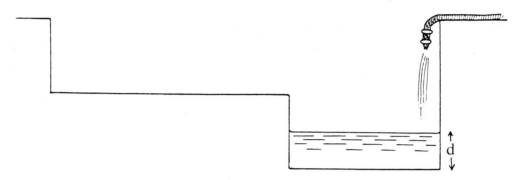

Describe fully, in words, how the depth (d) of water in the deep end of the pool varies with time, from the moment that the empty pool begins to fill.

_____

_____

_____

(ii) A different rectangular pool is being filled in a similar way.

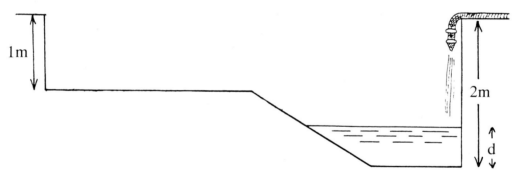

Sketch a graph to show how the depth (d) of water in the deep end of the pool varies with time, from the moment that the empty pool begins to fill. Assume that the pool takes thirty minutes to fill to the brim.

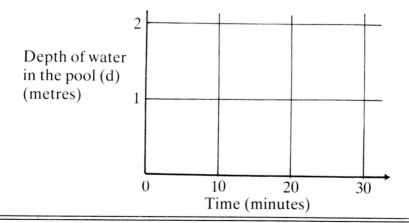

52

FILLING A SWIMMING POOL...MARKING SCHEME

(i)   **Describing a functional relationship using words.**

1 mark   For stating that d increases 'uniformly' or 'steadily' for the first part of the filling.

1 mark   for stating that there is a change in the rate at which d increases.

1 mark   for stating that d increases more slowly for the second part of the filling.

1 mark   for stating that d increases 'uniformly' or 'steadily' in the second part of the filling.

(ii)   **Translating a function presented pictorially into graphical form.**

1 mark   if the first part of the graph is curved.

1 mark   if the first part is concave downwards.

1 mark   if the second part is a straight line with a positive gradient.

1 mark   if the sketch starts at $(0,0)$, finishes at $(30,2)$ and there is a change at $(x,1)$ where $5 \leqslant x \leqslant 10$.

If the graph consists of more than two parts, mark the first and last part, and deduct 1 mark from the total obtained.

Ignore any final part that is a horizontal straight line showing an overflow.

A total of 8 marks are available for this question.

Paul

It gets deeper at a constant quick speed until it reaches the longer but then it begin to fill up at a constant slower speed.

Christopher

It will fill at a constant speed up to the level part where it will fill less fast

Mark

To start with the pool will fill up relitivly fast until the other part (shallow) gets water in, then it will slow down tremendously.

Paul's description considers not only the fact that d increases at two rates but also that each rate is "constant". He was awarded the full 4 marks for his answer to part (i).

Christopher's description again considers the change in speed. However, although he has implied that for the first part of the pool, d increases at a constant rate, he has omitted this from the second part. He was therefore awarded 3 marks.

Mark has noted the fact that d increases at two rates, but he has not mentioned the fact that these rates are linear. He scored 2 marks.

Simon

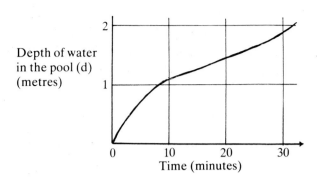

Mandy

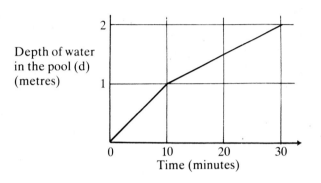

Beverley

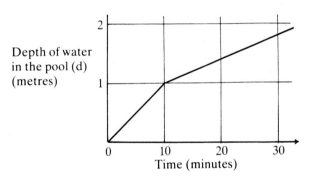

Katrina

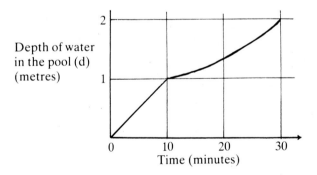

Andrew

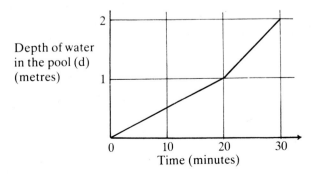

56

Simon's graph was awarded 3 marks out of a possible 4. His graph does not end at (30,2) and shows the change in rate occurring *after* 1 metre. Otherwise, his graph is correct.

Mandy was awarded only 2 marks, since the first part of her graph was not a concave downwards curve.

Beverley, Katrina and Andrew were each awarded 1 mark. Beverley's graph is similar to Mandy's but it does not end at (30,2). Katrina gained her mark for starting at (0,0), finishing at (30,2) and showing a change at (10,1). Andrew gained his mark for showing the second part as a straight line with a positive gradient.

Classroom Materials

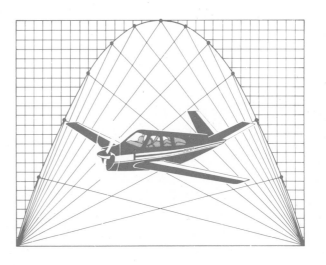

Classroom Materials

INTRODUCTION

These offer some resources by which pupils can be prepared for the questions on the examination. All the materials and suggestions are offered in the explicit recognition that every teacher will work in their own classroom in their own individual way.

The aims of the material are to develop and give pupils experience in
* interpreting graphs of practical situations
* sketching graphs from situations presented in verbal or pictorial form
* searching for patterns within situations, identifying functional relationships and expressing these verbally, graphically and algebraically
* using graphs to solve problems arising from realistic situations.

The classroom material is organised into two Units (A and B, each of which is intended to support roughly two weeks' work), together with a problem collection providing supplementary material for students who need further practice at interpreting information presented graphically and for students who enjoy the challenge of solving realistic problems.

Unit A contains a series of lesson suggestions which focus on the qualitative meaning of graphs set in realistic contexts, rather than on abstract technical skills associated with choosing scales, plotting points and drawing curves. (These skills are already thoroughly covered in most courses). This is because research evidence suggests that many pupils lack an understanding of the meaning of global graphical features such as maxima, minima, discontinuities, cyclical changes, increases or decreases over an interval, and gradients, when these are embedded in realistic contexts. Unit A contains almost no algebra, and has been used successfully with pupils in the top half of the ability range. (Some teachers have also used this Unit with pupils of low mathematical attainment, and have been encouraged by the results. However, in this case, a slower, more thorough approach was needed).

Unit B offers pupils the opportunity to discover and explore patterns and functions arising from realistic situations and relate these to algebraic expressions which include linear, reciprocal, quadratic and exponential functions. Unit B is technically more demanding than Unit A, and has been used successfully with pupils in the top quarter of the ability range.

The Problem Collection has been divided into two parts. The first provides nine problems, set in realistic contexts, for quicker or more able pupils to solve cooperatively. Each problem is accompanied by a separate selection of hints which may be supplied to groups who need more detailed guidance. Many of these problems are quite challenging, and are open to a variety of approaches—although a graphical solution is usually possible. The second part contains seven shorter situations which require more straightforward practice at interpreting data.

More detailed introductions to these Units are provided on pages 63, 109 and 143 respectively. You may also find it helpful to look at the **Support Materials** and to work through them with your colleagues if possible; they are in a section at the end of this book.

Notes for the teacher in each Unit provide specific teaching suggestions. Some of the activities involve class or group work and for this reason we have included some detailed suggestions on managing and promoting useful discussions between pupils. A summary of these suggestions may be found on the inside of the back cover to this book. As was emphasised earlier, all the teaching suggestions are offered in the recognition that every teacher will work in their classroom in their own individual way. The trials of the material established that teachers found it helpful to have explicit detailed suggestions which they could choose from and modify. All the material contained in this book has been used in a representative range of classrooms and has proved to be effective in developing the skills that are the concern of this module.

Throughout the Module, all pupils materials are "framed" and it is assumed that calculators will be available throughout. Masters of the worksheets for photocopying are enclosed in a separate pack.

Unit A

CONTENTS

INTRODUCTION

Unit A focuses on the qualitative meaning of graphs, rather than on technical skills associated with choosing scales, plotting points and drawing curves. (These skills are already thoroughly covered in most courses). This is because research evidence suggests that many pupils lack an understanding of the meaning of global graphical features such as maxima, minima, discontinuities, cyclical changes, increases or decreases over an interval, and gradients, when these are embedded in realistic contexts.

This Unit contains five lesson outlines, and is intended to occupy approximately two weeks.

A1 contains a number of activities which require pupils to reason qualitatively about the meaning of points located in the cartesian plane. Early items involve comparing positions and gradients, while later ones involve the consideration of correlation and a functional relationship.

A2 is designed to expose and provoke discussion about the common misconception that graphs are mere 'pictures' of the situations that they represent.

A3 contains activities which involve pupils in translating between verbal descriptions and sketch graphs.

A4 and A5 are both concerned with sketching and interpreting graphs from pictures of situations. Gradually, more sophisticated graphical features are presented. In particular, A4 involves interpreting maxima, minima, interval lengths and periodicity while A5 concentrates more on the interpretation of gradients.

At the end of this Unit we have included some further activities which may be used to supplement these booklets. They may be used, for example, as a homework resource.

A1 INTERPRETING POINTS

As you work through this booklet, discuss your answers with your neighbours and try to come to some agreement.

1. The Bus Stop Queue

Who is represented by each point on the scattergraph, below?

Alice   Brenda   Cathy   Dennis   Errol   Freda Gavin

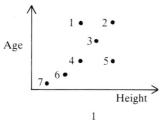

1

---

4. Sport

Suppose you were to choose, at random, 100 people and measure how heavy they are. You then ask them to perform in 3 sports;

High Jumping, Weight Lifting and Darts.

Sketch scattergraphs to show how you would expect the results to appear, and explain each graph, underneath. Clearly state any assumptions you make . . .

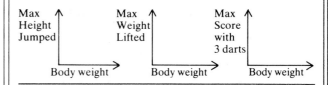

5. Shapes

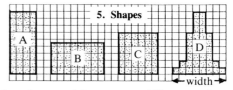

These four shapes each have an area of 36 square units.

* Label four points on the graph below, with the letters A, B, C and D.

* Can you draw a fifth shape, with an area of 36 square units, to correspond to the other point? Explain.

* Draw a scattergraph to show *every rectangle* with an area of 36 square units.

* Finally, what happens if you include *all* shapes, with the same area, on your graph?

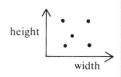

4

---

2. Two Aircraft

The following quick sketch graphs describe two light aircraft, A and B: (note: the graphs have *not* been drawn accurately)

The first graph shows that aircraft B is more expensive than aircraft A. What else does it say?

* Are the following statements true or false?

   "The older aircraft is cheaper"?
   "The faster aircraft is smaller"?
   "The larger aircraft is older"?
   "The cheaper aircraft carries fewer passengers"?

* Copy the graphs below. On each graph, mark and label two points to represent A and B.

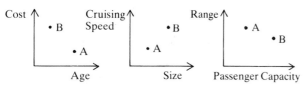

2

---

3. Telephone Calls

One weekend,
Five people made telephone calls to various part of the country.

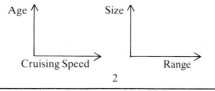

They recorded both the cost of their calls, and the length of time they were on the telephone, on the graph below:

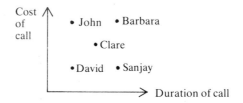

* Who was ringing long-distance? Explain your reasoning carefully.

* Who was making a local call? Again, explain.

* Which people were dialling roughly the same distance? Explain.

* Copy the graph and mark other points which show people making local calls of different durations.

* If you made a similar graph showing every phone call made in Britain during one particular week-end, what would it look like? Draw a sketch, and clearly state any assumptions you make.

3

A1 INTERPRETING POINTS

The aim of this booklet is to offer pupils an opportunity to discuss and reason about the qualitative meaning of points in the cartesian plane. Five situations are presented which involve progressively more sophisticated ideas, from straightforward comparisons of position (items 1 and 2), to comparisons involving gradients (item 3), and eventually to the consideration of correlation (item 4) and functional relationships (item 5). Between one and two hours will be needed.

Suggested Presentation

1. Issue the booklet, and *briefly* explain the purpose of this lesson (and of the following few lessons), perhaps as follows:

   "What does the topic 'Functions and Graphs' mean to you? Perhaps you immediately think of putting numbers into formulae, making tables, choosing scales, plotting points and then joining them up with straight lines or smooth curves. In the next few lessons, however, our approach will be quite different. Instead of starting with algebra, we will be starting with situations from everyday life (sport, telephone calls, etc) and exploring how even a quick sketch graph can be used to communicate a great deal of information, and sometimes save many written words of explanation. For this work, you will need to talk with your neighbours and try to decide together what the various graphs are saying."

2. Now allow pupils time to attempt the first three problems ("The bus stop queue", "Two aircraft" and "Telephone calls") in pairs or small groups. It is important that this is conducted in an atmosphere of discussion so that pupils are given every opportunity to explain and justify their own reasoning and receive feedback from others. Each group should be encouraged to discuss their ideas until they arrive at a consensus. Usually, the first two items cause less difficulty, whereas the third creates a great deal more discussion.

3. Tour the room, listening and inviting pupils to explain what they are doing. This will help them later, as they attempt to write down their own explanations. Before joining in a group discussion, we urge you to consult the inside back cover of this book, where we have provided a "Classroom discussion checklist" which contains a few suggestions concerning a teacher's role in promoting lively discussion. If pupils are making no progress then you may need to provide hints, but try to avoid giving too many heavily directed hints, like, for item 1, "Look at the points labelled 1 and 2. These represent the two oldest people. Which of these is taller?" Instead, give more strategic hints which encourage pupils to think for themselves, such as "How can you look at this graph more systematically?"

4. Several difficulties may emerge:

   • "There are no numbers on the axes!" This problem may cause difficulty to pupils whose only previous graphical experience concerned those technical skills associated with accurate point plotting. If we had included scales on the axes, pupils would have simply read off values, and answered the problem without considering the significance of the relative positions of the points. You may need to remind pupils of the normal convention—that quantities increase as we move across the page from left to right or vertically upwards.

- (on item 1) "I think that points 1 and 2 are Alice and Errol, and that 4 and 5 are Brenda and Dennis". Confusion is often caused by the fact that the height axis has not been placed vertically upwards. This is intentional in order to force pupils to look upon the graph as an abstract representation, rather than as a mere "picture", (ie, where "high" points are "tall" people). This common misconception is treated more fully in A2.

- You may also need to explain the meaning of several words in the booklet. In particular, 'scattergraph' (item 1), 'range' and 'passenger capacity' (item 2), and 'duration' (item 3) have been seen to cause some difficulty.

5. Towards the end of the lesson, you may feel the need to discuss item 3, "Telephone calls", with the class as a whole. This is the first item that requires an understanding of gradients and is therefore much more demanding. Below we indicate one way in which you may do this.

   If the class have been working in groups, call upon a representative from each group to explain their answers to the first three questions. As they do this, avoid passing an immediate judgement on their views as this may prevent other pupils from contributing alternative ideas. For example, in the dialogue below, the teacher allows pupils to continue putting forward their ideas even after a correct response has been received:

Teacher:	"Who was ringing long-distance?"
Pupil A:	"You can't tell because distance is not on the graph."
Teacher:	"Sarah, what did your group think?"
Pupil B:	"It's John."
Teacher:	"Explain why you think it's John."
Pupil B:	"Because he has to pay a lot for a short time."
Teacher:	"Thanks Sarah, now are there any other ideas?"
Pupil C:	"We think it's Barbara *and* John."
Teacher:	"Why?"
Pupil C:	"Because they pay the most, so they must be ringing the furthest . . ."

   This last misconception may never have been uncovered and discussed if the teacher had acknowledged Sarah's response as correct. As pupils explain their answers, ask other pupils to comment on these explanations.

6. The final two questions on the 'Telephone Calls' item are very demanding. Invite at least three representatives from the groups to sketch their ideas on the

blackboard and explain their reasoning. The graphs below are typical of what may be expected:

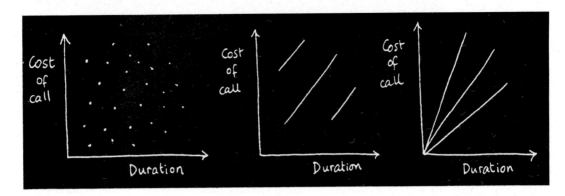

Invite members of other groups to criticise these graphs, and explain how they may be improved. If this proves difficult, then the following approach, adopted by one teacher during the trials, may be helpful. She began by redrawing the axes, marked and labelled a point "John", and then continued as follows:

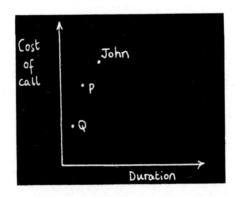

Teacher: "If you were to make a long distance call, where would you put *your* point on the scattergraph?"

Pupil A: "Below John and nearer to the cost line." (This pupil indicated point P).

Teacher: "Why did you put the point there?"

Pupil A: "Because if I talk for a shorter time than John, I don't have to pay as much as John."

Teacher: "If you made an even shorter call, where would you put that point?"

Pupil A indicated point Q.

Teacher: "Would these three points lie on a straight line or a curved line?"

Pupil A: "They have to be on a curved line, because otherwise the line would meet this line (the vertical axis), and you don't have to pay a lot of money not to talk."

Other pupils disagreed with this and insisted that the graph should be straight.

Pupil B: "It's straight because if you pay 5p for one minute, then you pay 10p for two minutes and . . ."

67

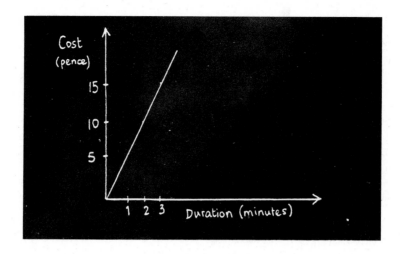

Then one group suggested the following, rather stunning insight:

Pupil C: "It isn't like that, because you have to pay the same amount of money when you pick up the phone and just say a word for, say, half a minute . . . you get this graph:"

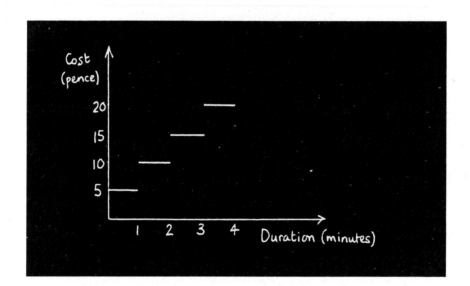

(We would not expect many pupils to reach this level of sophistication spontaneously, and in most cases we would advise you against imposing such a model upon the class, where it could cause considerable unnecessary confusion. For most purposes, the graph suggested by Pupil B is perfectly adequate. Most graphs are only 'models' of reality and as such they usually involve making simplifying assumptions, which should be stated.)
A long discussion ensued, and by the end of this lesson, most pupils appeared convinced by the step function. However, Pupil A still preferred a curved version:

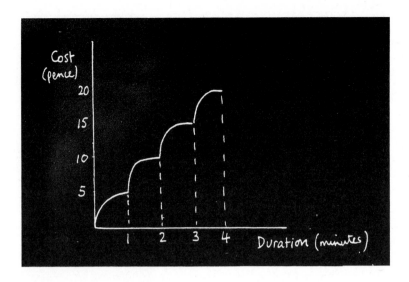

The teacher did not, in this case, impose 'the correct' answer on the class, as it didn't seem necessary. Such discussions do not always have to be resolved entirely in order for them to be valuable learning experiences. In many of these questions there is no single 'correct' answer anyway—it may all depend, as we have said, on the underlying assumptions.

7.   The remaining items in the booklet, 'Sport' and 'Shapes', can also cause a similar amount of debate. Below, we offer one possible development with item 5, "Shapes":

Ask everyone in the class to imagine a rectangle with an area of, say 36 square units. Draw the following graph on the blackboard, and place one point on it, explaining that this represents one such rectangle.

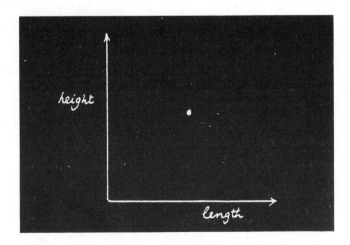

Now ask various pupils to describe where they would place points to represent their imagined rectangles. The following questions may help develop the discussion:

69

"Suppose I mark a point here".
(Indicate position A, but do not mark the blackboard).
"Can this represent a rectangle with the same area, 36 square units? Why?"
(Repeat this for positions
B, C, D, E and F).

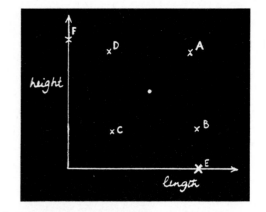

Can you identify other points on the graph which *cannot* represent rectangles with an area of 36 square units? Suppose we mark in *all* such points—in which "forbidden" regions will they lie?

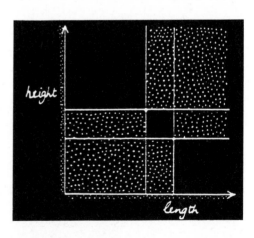

Let's mark in another point which *can* represent such a rectangle. Are there any new "forbidden" regions?

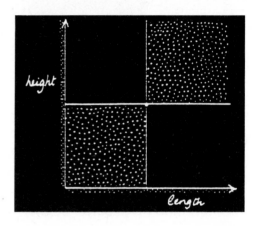

Suppose we continue in this way, shading in "forbidden" regions each time . . .

Such a discussion may lead to an awareness that all points which represent rectangles with an area of 36 square units, will lie on a connected, curved, line. (It cannot be straight or it would meet an axis - giving a rectangle with zero area).

If the "rectangular" constraint is now lifted, (and any shape is allowed, providing it has an area of 36 square units), the discussion can be developed still further. It may, for example, lead to such questions as:

"Can we have a shape with a very large (infinite?) length and height, and yet still with an area of 36 square units?"

A1   SOME SOLUTIONS

Note: In these solutions, as in all other solutions in this Module, there are often several correct alternatives, depending upon the underlying assumptions made or upon the degree of sophistication desired. In many cases the sketch graphs given, which are only intended as approximate models, may be further refined (using step functions, for example) to give more accurate representations. These solutions only attempt to represent a collection of acceptable responses achievable by an able pupil. They are in no way supposed to represent definitive, exhaustive analyses of the items.

1.   The Bus Stop Queue

Alice is represented by point 2

Brenda is represented by point 4

Cathy is represented by point 6

Dennis is represented by point 1

Errol is represented by point 5

Freda is represented by point 3

Gavin is represented by point 7

2.   Two Aircraft

The first graph also states that aircraft A is older than aircraft B.

The following two statements are true:

"The older aircraft is cheaper."

"The cheaper aircraft carries few passengers."

The final two graphs should appear as below:

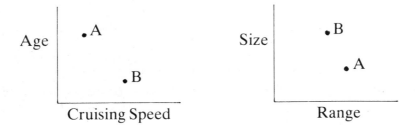

71

3. Telephone Calls

John was ringing long distance. (Short time, high cost).

Sanjay was making a local call. (Long time, low cost).

David, Clare and Barbara were dialling roughly the same distance (assuming that the cost is proportional to the time).

Other local calls will fall in a straight line which passes through Sanjay's point and the origin. At the time of writing, three charge rates operate at weekends; for local calls (L), for calls up to 56 km (a) and for calls over 56 km (b). (Here, we neglect calls to the Channel Islands, Northern Ireland and Overseas.) The graph showing every telephone call made in Britain during one weekend would therefore look like:

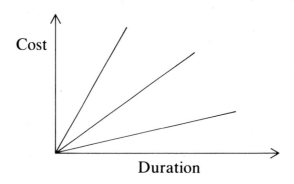

This again, of course, assumes that the cost is proportional to the time. (As costs can only be paid in discrete amounts, a more sophisticated model would involve a step-function).

4. Sport

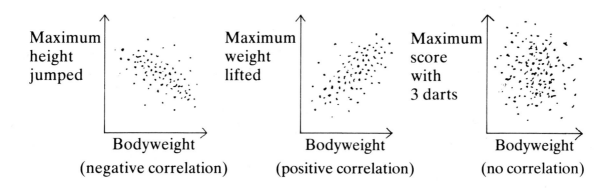

In sketching these very rough graphs, we have assumed a random sample of people from roughly the same adult age group. If, for example, very young children are included, the graphs will be quite different. Pupils may also point out that many expert darts players are overweight, due perhaps to the nature of their training environment!

5. Shapes

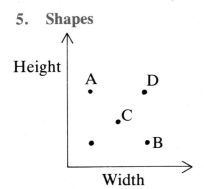

No shape with an area of 36 square units can correspond to the fifth point. As both of its dimensions are less than those of point C, it can be seen that this shape must lie *within* a 6 by 6 square.

If *every* rectangle with an area of 36 square units is plotted on the same graph, we obtain the rectangular hyperbola:

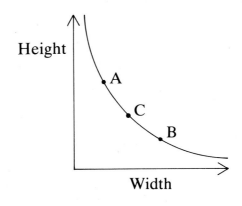

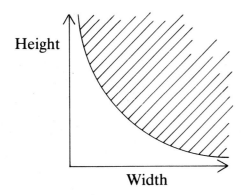

If *all* shapes with the same area are plotted, then we will obtain the shaded region above this hyperbola.

A2 ARE GRAPHS JUST PICTURES?

Golf Shot

How does the speed of the ball change as it flies through the air in this amazing golf shot?

* Discuss this situation with your neighbour, and write down a clear description stating how you both think the speed of the golf ball changes.

* Now sketch a rough graph to illustrate your description:

Speed
of
the
ball

Time after the ball is hit by the golf club.

1

Peter attempted the golf question and produced a graph like this:

Speed of ball

Time after ball is hit

* Comment on it.

* Can you suggest *why* Peter drew his graph like this?

* Can you see any connection between Peter's attempt and the cartoon on page 1?

Now try the problem below:

Roller-coaster

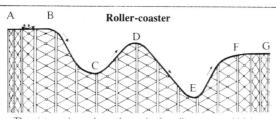

The picture above shows the track of a roller-coaster, which is travelling at a slow constant speed between A and B. How will the speed of this roller-coaster vary as it travels along the track from A to G?

Describe your answer both in words and by sketching a graph in your book.

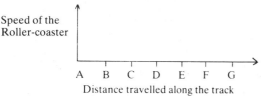

Speed of the
Roller-coaster

A B C D E F G
Distance travelled along the track

2

Finally, discuss and write about this problem:

Which Sport?

Which sport will produce a graph like this?

Choose the best answer from the following and explain exactly how it fits the graph.

Write down reasons why you reject alternatives.

Fishing
Pole Vaulting
100 metre Sprint
Sky Diving
Golf
Archery
Javelin Throwing
High Jumping
High Diving
Snooker
Drag Racing
Water Skiing

4

This next activity will help you to see how well you have drawn your sketch graph.

Fold this booklet so that you cannot see the picture of the roller-coaster track.

Try to answer the following questions using *only your sketch graph.*

* Along which parts of the track was the roller-coaster travelling quickly? slowly?

* Was the roller-coaster travelling faster at B or D? D or F? C or E?

* Where was the roller-coaster accelerating (speeding up)? decelerating (slowing down)?

Check your answers to these questions by looking back at the picture of the roller-coaster track. If you find any mistakes, *redraw* your sketch graph. (It is better to use a fresh diagram than to try and correct your first attempt.)

* Now invent some roller-coaster tracks of your own.
Sketch a graph for each one, on a separate sheet of paper. Pass *only the sketch graphs* to your neighbour.
Can she reconstruct the shape of the original roller-coaster tracks?

* Do you notice any connection between the shape of a roller-coaster track, and the shape of its graph? If so write down an explanation.
Are there any exceptions?

3

74

A2   ARE GRAPHS JUST PICTURES?

Many pupils, unable to treat graphs as abstract representations of relationships, appear to interpret them as if they are mere "pictures" of the underlying situations. This booklet is designed to expose and provoke discussion about this common misconception, so that pupils are alerted to possible errors in graphical interpretation which may result.

Approximately one hour will be needed.

Suggested Presentation

1. Issue the booklet and explain the introductory situation. Ask the class to discuss this situation in pairs or small groups, until they come to some consensus. Then encourage each group to *write down* a clear description showing how they think the speed of the golf ball varies as it flies through the air, and then illustrate this description using a sketch graph.

2. As pupils work on the problem, tour the room and listen to what they are saying. You may find that some pupils confuse the *speed* of the ball with the *height* of the ball and produce statements like

    "The ball *speeds up* after it has been hit by the golf club."

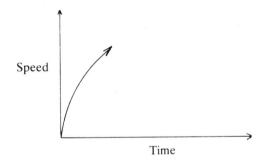

    They may feel that if the path of the ball goes 'up and down', then the graph should also go 'up and down'! (This is further reinforced by the fact that the ball begins and ends at rest!). Avoid condemning such responses, but rather invite comments from other pupils, and try to provoke "conflicts"—where pupils are made aware of inconsistencies in their own beliefs—by using questions like:

    "Where is the ball travelling most slowly?"
    "Does your graph agree with this?"

3. After ten minutes or so, you may feel the need to hold a short class discussion. During this, it is quite easy to become bogged down in discussing the "physics" of the situation, and become immersed in long debates concerning the nature of gravity and so on. Try to resist this. It is *not* essential that everyone arrives at the "perfect" graph—only that everyone is alerted to the danger of treating the graph as a mere picture of the situation. Therefore, do not feel that the discussion has to be fully resolved before moving onto the "Roller-coaster" item.

75

Begin the discussion by inviting representatives from two or three groups to sketch their graphs on the blackboard, and explain their reasoning. Do not pass judgement on them, but invite comments from the rest of the class.

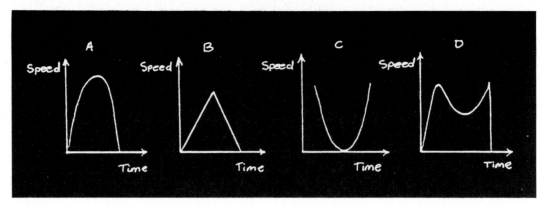

Pupil A: "We think it's A because the ball goes up and comes down."

Pupil B: "It's B because the ball slows down as it goes up, and speeds up as it goes down."

Pupil C: "In C, the ball starts off fast, then stops for a 'split second', then goes faster again."

Pupil D: "In D, the ball speeds up after it is hit, then slows down, then speeds up again and then falls into the hole."

These four (genuine) responses illustrate the kind of reasoning that can be expected. Notice that pupil A has our classical "graph = picture" misconception, pupil B cannot translate a perfectly valid explanation into a graph (a common occurrence), pupil C has assumed that the ball becomes stationary at the highest point of the trajectory and Pupil D has assumed that the ball accelerates after it leaves the club face.

In order to conclude the discussion, you may need to draw a fresh diagram on the blackboard showing the trajectory of the ball, and a pair of axes:

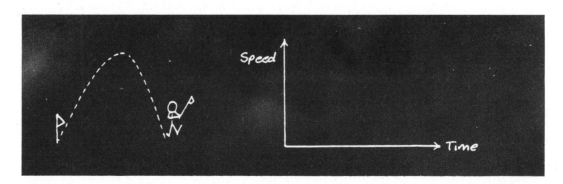

Trace the path of the ball with your hand and ask pupils to describe what happens to the ball's speed. As they make suggestions, ask them where the corresponding points on the graph should go. In this way it should be possible for everyone to see that the path of the ball and the shape of the graph are completely dissimilar. Do not worry if the resulting graph is not completely correct—the "Roller-coaster" situation will help to clear up any remaining misunderstandings.

4. Now ask pupils to turn over and continue working on the booklet, again in pairs or small groups. The "Roller-coaster" situation reinforces the difference between a "picture" of the track and a graph. When drawing the speed-distance graph, some pupils may still be unable to vary things in a continuous manner, and prefer to plot a few discrete points and join them up. This often results in a few bouts of "straight-line-itis":

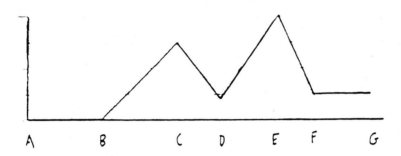

This is extremely common among pupils who have been introduced to graphs in the conventional, point plotting way.

5. It is important to emphasise that pupils may need to make several attempts at sketching a graph before they arrive at a correct version. Discourage them from erasing mistakes, but rather ask them to note down what is wrong with their sketch and draw a fresh one underneath. This will enable both the pupil and the teacher to monitor growth in understanding, and will help the pupil to treat each attempt as a helpful step towards a final solution.

6. In the booklet, it is suggested that pupils should be given the opportunity to invent their own roller-coaster tracks, sketch corresponding graphs and then see if their neighbour can reconstruct the shape of the original tracks from the graphs alone. As well as being enjoyable, this activity also emphasises the importance of *communicating* information accurately.

7. After a while, pupils may come to realise the following generalisation:

The connection between the graph and the rollercoaster is that the graph should look like the rollercoaster turned upside down.

However, others may be able to find exceptions:

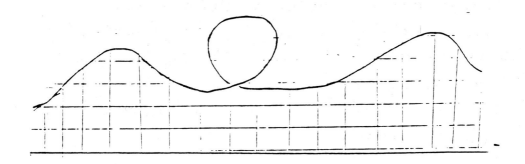

8.   The final activity in the booklet, "Which Sport?", is again intended to provoke a lively discussion. The following collection of answers (taken from the same class) illustrate the range of answers that may be expected.

Susan

(I think it is a horse. jumping. The horse canters up jumps). Sorry had second thoughts
Its a shotput the put is thrown up it travels and drops, then rolls It just reminded me of a shotput.

Joanne

I think this graph shows what a polevaulter would do because it shows the height of the vault and then they would have a sharp drop like the graph shows.

Tony

I think the sport is football because at the beginning of the game all the players are lively and not so weak but as the game is nearly over the player strength drops and stay at a steady ~~level~~ level till the game ends.

78

Greg

I have Reasons to believe that it will be a
Parachuties because the plane goes up and then
along the parachuties jumps out of the plane
and lands then he goes for a walk. Or
a diver who climbs up a cliff and dives of and
then starts swimming.

The Golf Shot

The speed of the ball will vary
roughly as shown in this graph:

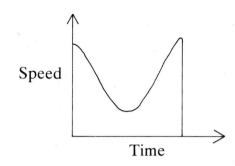

The Roller Coaster

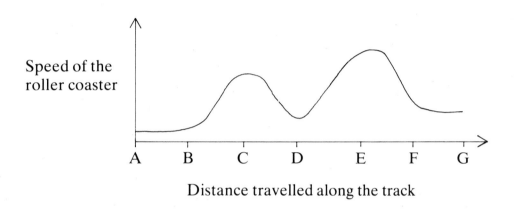

Distance travelled along the track

Notice that the sketch graph looks rather like an 'upside-down' picture of the track. This can create a powerful conflict due to the "graph = picture" misconception.

Which Sport?

Sky diving provides one plausible answer because it clearly shows:

* the acceleration as the diver falls,
* the terminal velocity as the wind resistance becomes equal to the gravitational pull,
* the rapid deceleration as the parachute opens,
* the steady float down and
* the 'bump' as he hits the ground.

Some may argue that the parachutist will not begin his fall with zero speed because of the horizontal motion of the aircraft. The graph does fit, however, if 'speed' is taken to mean *vertical* speed.

Sky diving may not be the only correct possibility, however. One pupil suggested that the graph could represent Fishing, where the speed of the hook is considered. As the line is cast, the hook accelerates, rapidly slows down as it enters the water, drifts along with the current and then stops suddenly when the line becomes taut.

Pole Vaulting, Golf, High Jumping, Javelin Throwing and Show Jumping all fail because the speed *decreases* as the athlete, ball, javelin or horse rises through the air, and *increases* again as they descend. Thus there will be a local minimum on the speed graph at the highest point of the trajectory.

A3 SKETCHING GRAPHS FROM WORDS

Picking Strawberries

The more people we get to help, the sooner we'll finish picking these strawberries.

STRAWBERRY PICKERS WANTED

* Using axes like the ones below, sketch a graph to illustrate this situation.

Total time it will take to finish the job

Number of people picking strawberries

* Compare your graph with those drawn by your neighbours. Try to come to some agreement over a correct version.

* Write down an explanation of how you arrived at your answer. In particular, answer the following three questions.

— should the graph 'slope upwards' or 'slope downwards'? Why?

— should the graph be a straight line? Why?

— should the graph meet the axes? If so, where? If not, why not?

1

Sketch graphs to illustrate the following statements. Label your axes with the variables shown in brackets. For the last statement you are asked to sketch two graphs on the same axes.

"In the spring, my lawn grew very quickly and it needed cutting every week, but since we have had this hot dry spell it needs cutting less frequently."

(length of grass/time)

"When doing a jigsaw puzzle, I usually spend the first half an hour or so just sorting out the edge pieces. When I have collected together all the ones I can find, I construct a border around the edge of the table. Then I start to fill in the border with the centre pieces. At first this is very slow going but the more pieces you put in, the less you have to sort through and so the faster you get."

(number of pieces put in jigsaw/time).

"The Australian cottony cushion scale insect was accidentally introduced into America in 1868 and increased in number until it seemed about to destroy the Californian citrus orchards where it lived. Its natural predator, a ladybird, was artificially introduced in 1889 and this quickly reduced the scale insect population. Later, DDT was used to try to cut down the scale insect population still further. However, the net result was to *increase* their numbers as, unfortunately, the ladybird was far more susceptible to DDT than the scale insect! For the first time in fifty years the scale insect again became a serious problem."
Use the same axes . . .
(scale insect population/time); (ladybird population/time).

4

Choose the best graph to fit each of the ten situations described below. (Particular graphs may fit more than one situation.) Copy the graph, label your axes and explain your choice, stating any assumptions you make. If you cannot find the graph you want, draw your own version.

1. "Prices are now rising more slowly than at any time during the last five years."

2. "I quite enjoy cold milk or hot milk, but I loathe lukewarm milk!"

3. "The smaller the boxes are, then the more boxes we can load into the van."

4. "After the concert there was a stunned silence. Then one person in the audience began to clap. Gradually, those around her joined in and soon everyone was applauding and cheering."

5. "If cinema admission charges are too low, then the owners will lose money. On the other hand, if they are too high then few people will attend and again they will lose. A cinema must therefore charge a moderate price in order to stay profitable."

In the following situations, *you* have to decide what happens. Explain them carefully in words, and choose the best graph, as before.

How does . . .

6. the cost of a bag of potatoes depend on its weight?

7. the diameter of a balloon vary as air is slowly released from it?

8. the time for running a race depend upon the length of the race?

2

---

9. the speed of a girl vary on a swing?

10. the speed of a ball vary as it bounces along?

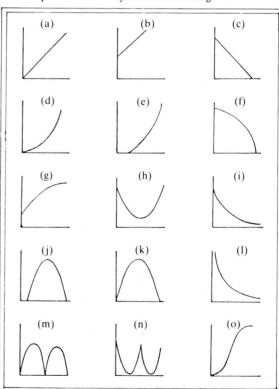

3

A3 SKETCHING GRAPHS FROM WORDS

In this booklet, pupils are invited to translate between verbal descriptions and sketch graphs. Two kinds of verbal forms are used: "Full descriptions" which give an explicit, detailed account of exactly how the variables relate to each other and "Trigger phrases" which ask the pupils to imagine a situation and then decide *for themselves* the nature of the relationship between the variables. Within either kind of presentation, there exists a considerable variation in difficulty, depending on the context, the language used, and the kinds of graphical features demanded. Between one and two hours will be needed.

Suggested Presentation

1. Issue the booklet and allow pupils time to discuss the introductory graph sketching activity in pairs or small groups, and encourage them to arrive at a consensus. Emphasise the need to write down an explanation of how they arrived at their answer, and draw their attention to the three questions at the foot of the page. As they work on this, tour the room listening and asking them to explain their reasoning—but at this stage it is better not to supply them with any answers, as this may spoil the class discussion which follows.

2. You may like to ask three or four representatives from the groups to sketch their graphs on the blackboard. Try to arrange this so that different graphs are represented, including the following if possible:

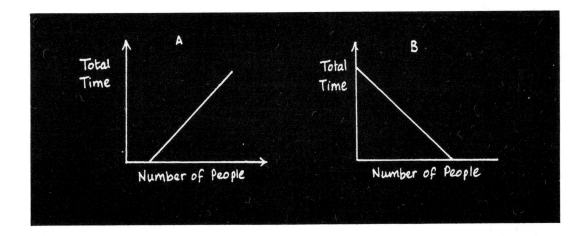

Ask the groups to explain their decisions and invite comments from others. For example, graph A (or a similar kind of increasing function) is sometimes chosen because pupils have misinterpreted the axes:

> "At the beginning, few people are picking strawberries, but as time goes on, more and more join in."

This misinterpretation has assumed that the vertical axis reads "elapsed time" rather than the "total time to finish the job." If this occurs, emphasise that this particular situation is different to those presented in A2 in that here it is *not* possible to trace a finger along the line of the graph and imagine time passing, because each point on the graph represents a different possible event. If pupils choose graph B, then the following development may be helpful:

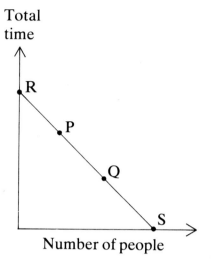

Teacher: "What does this point mean?" (Point P).

Pupil: "If you've only got a few people picking straw-berries then it will take a long time."

Teacher: "... and this point?" (Point Q).

Pupil: "If there are lots of people, it doesn't take so long."

Teacher: "What about this point?" (Point R) "... and this point?" (Point S).

This kind of questioning should enable the pupils to see that the graph cannot meet either axis. Some may decide that the graph should therefore be curved. Others may prefer to simply erase the two ends:

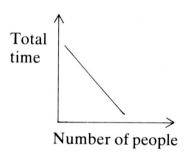

If this is suggested, ask pupils to consider what would happen if *very* many people are involved in picking strawberries. This should enable most pupils to see that the right hand end of the graph cannot terminate in this way.

When the left hand end is considered, however, pupils may raise the issue that "it is silly to have, say, half a person picking strawberries—so the graph must start with one person." (If, "number of people" is read to mean "number of people who work at a given rate", then it is just conceivable that the "fractional people" could be "lazy people!"). If *pupils* raise such issues, however, is it worth mentioning that the graph really only consists of discrete points;

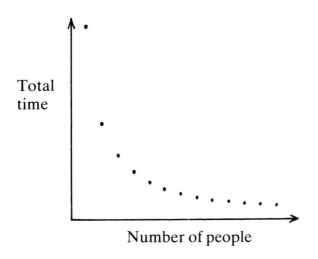

Total time

Number of people

As before, with the step functions in A1 for example, it is *not* essential to develop the graph to this degree of sophistication.

Occasionally, pupils may raise the following insight:

"If you double the number of people picking strawberries, you halve the time it takes."

This leads to the following sequence of points (P_1, P_2, . . .) which may settle once and for all the question of whether the graph is linear or curved:

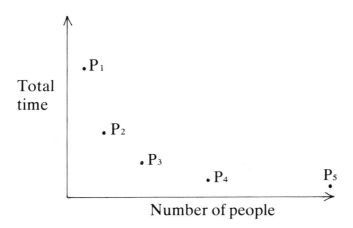

Total time

. P_1

. P_2

. P_3

. P_4 P_5

Number of people

3. After the discussion, ask the class to write down a full explanation of the correct sketch graph, using the outline given at the foot of the first page in the booklet.

4. Now encourage pupils to work through pages 2 and 3 of the booklet, matching the situations to the graphs. Emphasise the importance of labelling axes, writing explanations and stating assumptions. Again, group discussion is essential if pupils are to improve in their understanding. This will take time and you should not worry if progress seems slow. (You may like to suggest that pupils work on, say, the odd numbered questions during the lesson, and leave the even numbered questions for homework).

In this exercise, pupils may soon notice, in discussion with their neighbours, that several different sketch graphs may be made to fit a particular situation—depending on the labelling of the axes and the assumptions made. For example, for the first item, "Prices are now rising more slowly than at any time during the last five years", the following graphs are *all* valid solutions.

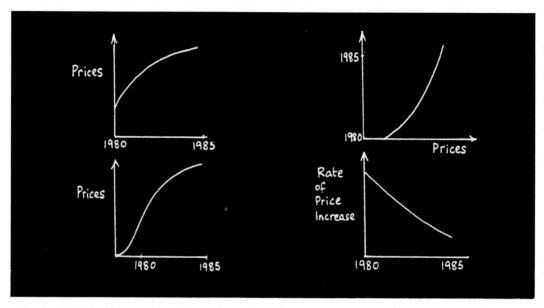

This multiplicity of answers may make full class discussion a bewildering experience, unless it is based on few questions, dealt with slowly and thoroughly. It is probably more helpful to coach the pupils on an individual or group basis. Often, it is enough to simply read through the question again with a pupil, and then run your finger along their graph and ask them what it is saying. This often helps them to see discrepancies in their solution.

5. The remaining items in the booklet, on page 4, invite pupils to attempt to sketch graphs with a wider variety of features. As the axes are now specified, there are fewer possible solutions which make them more amenable to class discussion, if it is felt necessary.

A3 Some Solutions

Page 1: A 'correct' graph for the introductory situation has the following shape:

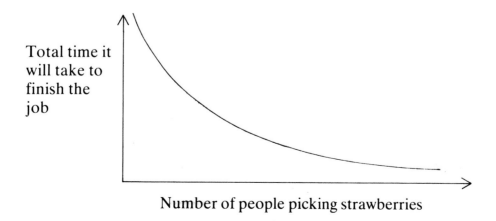

Number of people picking strawberries

(As has been mentioned before, a more refined model should consist of a set of discrete points. Also, if the number of people involved becomes very large, there is also the possibility that they will get in each others' way, and thus force the graph upwards again. Both of these refinements need not be emphasised to pupils, unless they raise such issues themselves).

Page 2: The situations can be paired off with the graphs as follows (but as explained in the teacher's notes, there are many other possibilities and further refinements).

1 and (g) (Prices against Time)   6 and (a) (Cost against Weight)
2 and (h) (Enjoyment against Temperature)   7 and (f) (Diameter against Time)
3 and (l) (Number against Size)   8 and (d) (Time against Length of race)
4 and (o) (Number clapping against Time)   9 and (m) (Speed against Time)
5 and (j) (Profit made against Price of admission) 10 and (n) (Speed against Time)

Page 4: The final three situations may be illustrated with graphs as shown below:

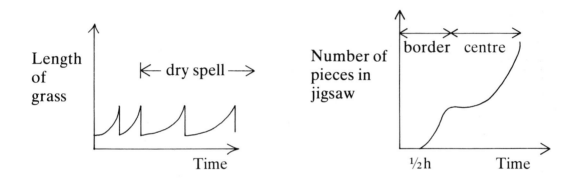

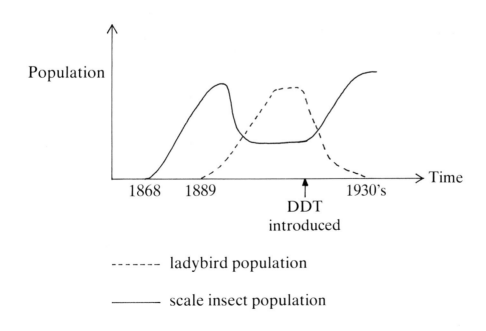

------- ladybird population

———— scale insect population

(Note that the relative heights of these graphs is unimportant).

87

A4 SKETCHING GRAPHS FROM PICTURES

Motor Racing

How do you think the speed of a racing car will vary as it travels on the *second lap* around each of the three circuits drawn below? (S = starting point)

Circuit 1   Circuit 2   Circuit 3

Explain your answer in each case both in words and with a sketch graph. State clearly any assumptions that you make.

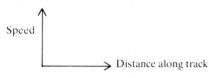

Speed

Distance along track

Compare your graphs with those produced by your neighbours. Try to produce three graphs which you all agree are correct.

1

The Big Wheel

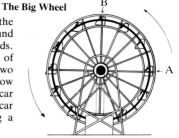

The Big Wheel in the diagram turns round once every 20 seconds. On the same pair of axes, sketch two graphs to show how both the height of car A and the height of car B will vary during a minute.

Describe how your graphs will change if the wheel turns more quickly.

Orbits

Each of the diagrams below shows a spacecraft orbiting a planet at a constant speed.
Sketch two graphs to show how the distance of the spacecraft from the planet will vary with time.

Using a dotted line on the same axes, show how your graphs will change if the speed of the spacecraft increases as it gets nearer to the planet.

Now invent your own orbits and sketch their graphs, *on a separate sheet of paper*. Give *only* your graphs to your neighbour. Can she reconstruct the orbits from the graphs alone? 4

Look again at the graph you drew for the third circuit. In order to discover how good your sketch is, answer the following questions looking *only* at your sketch graph. When you have done this, check your answer by looking back at the picture of the circuit. If you find any mistakes *redraw* your sketch graph.

— Is the car on the first or second lap?

— How many bends are there on the circuit?

— Which bend is the most dangerous?

— Which "straight" portion of the circuit is the longest? Which is the shortest?

— Does the car begin the third lap with the same speed as it began the second? Should it?

Now invent a racing circuit of your own with, at most, four bends.

Sketch a graph *on a separate sheet of paper* to show how the speed of a car will vary as it goes around your circuit.

Pass *only* your graph to your neighbour.

Can she reconstruct the shape of the original racing circuit?

2

The graph below shows how the speed of a racing car varies during the second lap of a race.

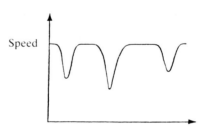

Speed

Distance along the track

Which of these circuits was it going round?

Discuss this problem with your neighbours.
Write down your reasons each time you reject a circuit.

3

A4 SKETCHING GRAPHS FROM PICTURES

In this booklet we offer pupils the opportunity to discuss the meaning of various graphical features, (including maxima, minima and periodicity), in three realistic contexts. We also aim to give pupils a greater awareness of how to approach sketching a graph when many situational factors have to be taken into account simultaneously. Approximately one hour will be needed.

Suggested Presentation

1. Allow the pupils about ten minutes to discuss the situation on the first page of the booklet, in pairs or small groups. While they do this, draw a simple racetrack on the blackboard. (It need not be the same one as in the booklet):

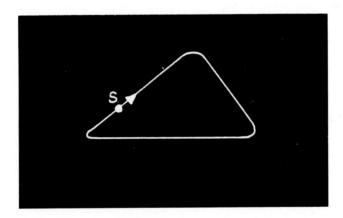

2. Now invite a volunteer to describe, verbally, how the speed of the car will vary as it travels around this track. (Discourage her from introducing too many technical details, such as gear changing, at this stage). Ask this pupil to sketch a speed-distance graph on the blackboard, and invite criticism from other members of the class.

3. As each pupil passes a comment, invite them to come out and sketch a fresh graph under the previous one, explaining what new consideration they have taken into account. In this way, the original graph can be successively improved until everyone is satisfied that it fully describes the situation.

4. Emphasise that when sketching graphs, pupils should not expect to get perfect sketches immediately, but must expect to have to make several attempts. Discourage pupils from erasing mistakes, but rather ask them to *write down* what is wrong with their sketch, and draw a fresh one underneath.

For example:

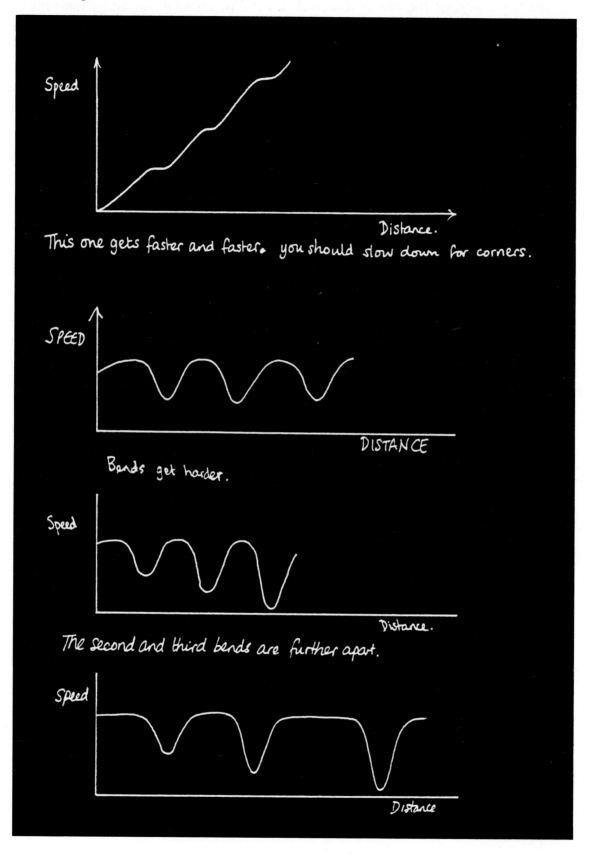

This one gets faster and faster. you should slow down for corners.

Bends get harder.

The second and third bends are further apart.

5. Now encourage the pupils to continue with the booklet, inventing their own circuits, and choosing the correct circuit to match the graph on page 3.

6. The final page of the booklet contains two situations which are of a periodic nature. (If time is particularly short, then these may be used to provide suitable homework material).

A4   SOME SOLUTIONS

page 1: **Motor Racing**

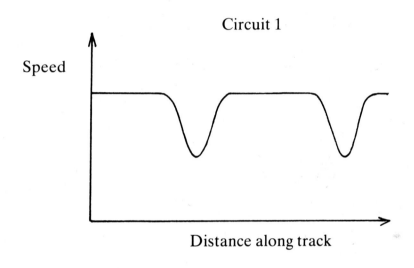

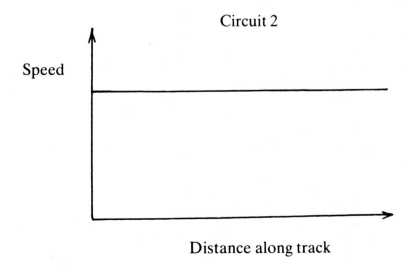

Circuit 3

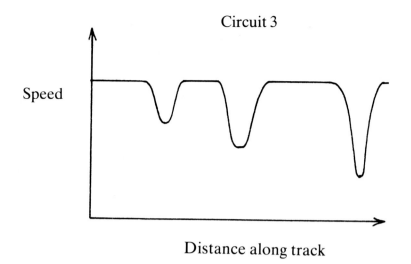

Speed

Distance along track

page 3: The car was travelling around circuit C.
Circuits A, E and G have too many bends.
Circuits B and D are ruled out because the second bend should be the most difficult.
Circuit F is ruled out because the longest 'straight' should occur between the second and third bends.

page 4: **The Big Wheel**

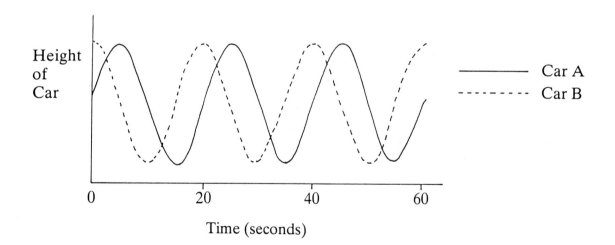

Height of Car

Time (seconds)

——————— Car A
- - - - - - - Car B

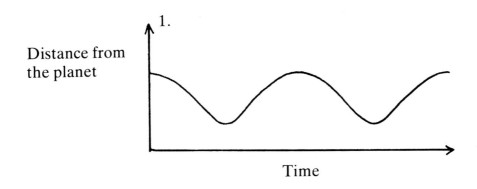

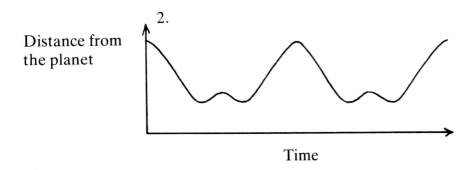

(These graphs assume that the spacecraft is travelling at a constant speed).

A5 LOOKING AT GRADIENTS

Filling Bottles

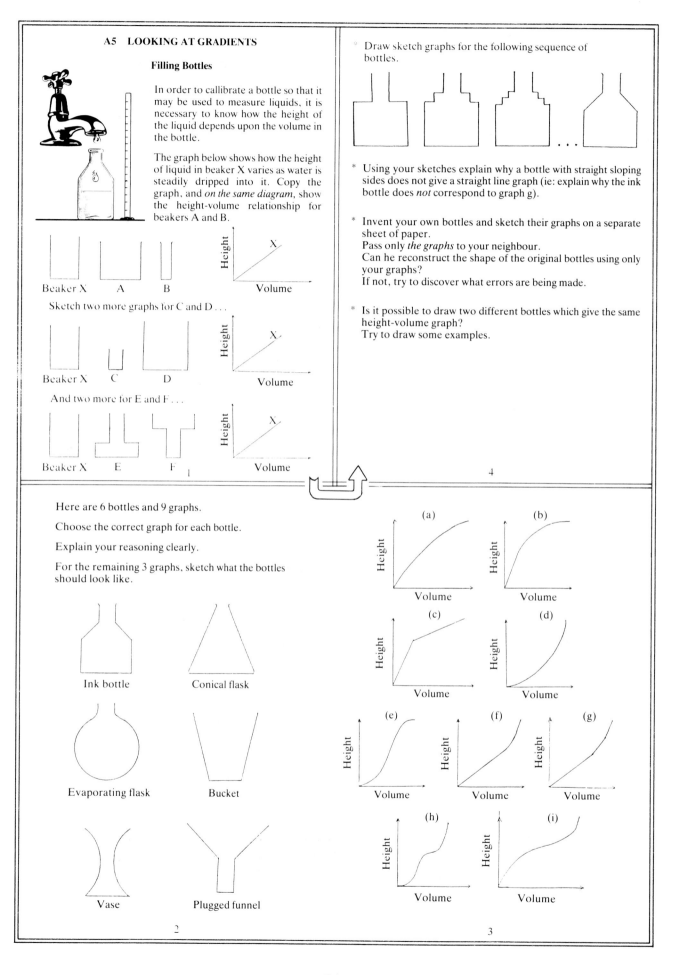

In order to callibrate a bottle so that it may be used to measure liquids, it is necessary to know how the height of the liquid depends upon the volume in the bottle.

The graph below shows how the height of liquid in beaker X varies as water is steadily dripped into it. Copy the graph, and *on the same diagram*, show the height-volume relationship for beakers A and B.

Beaker X   A   B

Sketch two more graphs for C and D . . .

Beaker X   C   D

And two more for E and F . . .

Beaker X   E   F

Draw sketch graphs for the following sequence of bottles.

* Using your sketches explain why a bottle with straight sloping sides does not give a straight line graph (ie: explain why the ink bottle does *not* correspond to graph g).

* Invent your own bottles and sketch their graphs on a separate sheet of paper.
Pass only *the graphs* to your neighbour.
Can he reconstruct the shape of the original bottles using only your graphs?
If not, try to discover what errors are being made.

* Is it possible to draw two different bottles which give the same height-volume graph?
Try to draw some examples.

Here are 6 bottles and 9 graphs.

Choose the correct graph for each bottle.

Explain your reasoning clearly.

For the remaining 3 graphs, sketch what the bottles should look like.

Ink bottle   Conical flask

Evaporating flask   Bucket

Vase   Plugged funnel

(a) (b) (c) (d) (e) (f) (g) (h) (i)

A5 LOOKING AT GRADIENTS

The situation, 'Filling Bottles' provides a harder challenge than most of the preceding ones, because it focuses mainly on sketching and interpreting *gradients*. The microcomputer program, "Bottles", (provided within the support material to this Module) may be used to enhance this presentation. Approximately one hour will be needed.

Suggested Presentation

1. Ask the pupils to imagine themselves filling up a milk bottle at the kitchen sink. What happens? When does the water level rise slowly? Why is this? Why does the water tend to spurt out of the bottle at the top? (If at all possible, borrow a selection of bottles from the science department, and discuss how each of them will fill, perhaps demonstrating this by pouring water steadily into each one and asking the class to describe and explain what they see). In this way, try to focus their attention on how the water level in each bottle depends upon the volume of water poured in.

2. Now issue the booklet.

    You may need to explain the opening paragraph. Ask the class if they have seen calibrated bottles in their science lessons. Ask pupils to explain why, for example, calibrations on a conical flask get further apart towards the top of the bottle. What would the calibrations on the evaporating flask look like? Why?

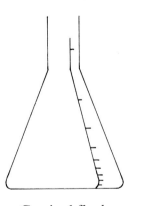
Conical flask

Evaporating flask

3. Pupils should now attempt the worksheets in pairs or groups. In the exercise where the bottles have to be matched with the graphs, each pair or group should be asked to discuss the situation until they arrive at a consensus.

4. The following stepwise approach can be of considerable help to those who are in difficulty.

    "Imagine you increase the volume by equal amounts. What happens to the height of the liquid in the bottle?"

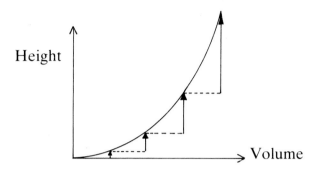

(In this case, the height increases by a small amount to start with (so the bottle must be wide here), and gradually rises by larger and larger amounts (so the bottle must gradually get narrower). This graph therefore, corresponds to the conical flask.

5. As you tour the room, you may notice that many pupils believe that graph (g) corresponds to the ink bottle, and graph (c) corresponds to the plugged funnel. This is probably due to a feeling that a "straight" edge on the bottle must correspond to a straight line on the graph (our old friend the 'graph = picture' misconception). Similarly, many pupils choose graph (e), graph (h) or even graph (d) for the evaporating flask, because the concave curve on the lower part of the bottle is identified with the concave graph. The final page of the booklet attempts to help pupils overcome such misconceptions, so it may be worth delaying a discussion about pages 2 and 3 until everyone has had a chance to discover and explain their own errors, on page 4. This page asks pupils to sketch graphs for the following sequence of bottles:

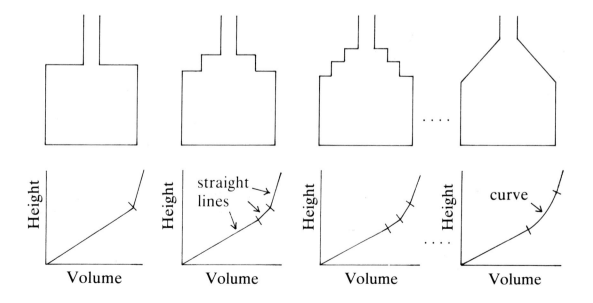

This may enable them to see that graph (f) rather than graph (g) should correspond to the ink bottle.

6. Finally, encourage pupils to invent their own bottles, sketch corresponding graphs, and then see if their neighbours can reconstruct the shapes of the original bottles from the graphs alone.

    Pupils may also discover that different bottles can result in the same graph:

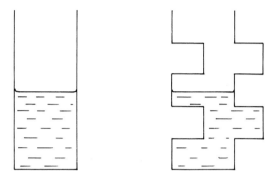

    This does of course assume that bottles without axial symmetry may be used.

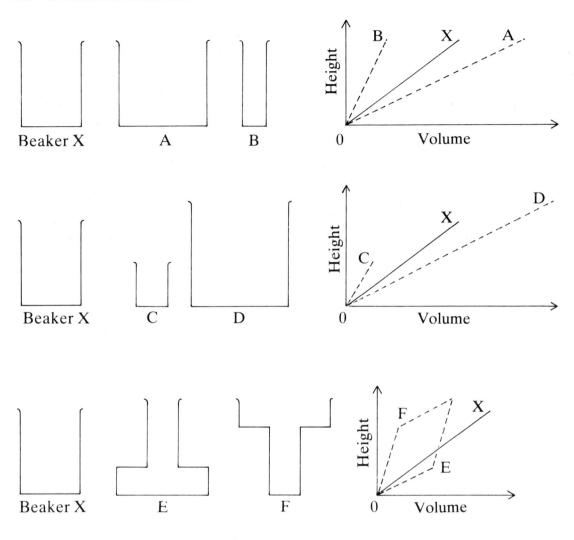

The pairs are: Ink bottle—(f)
Conical flask—(d)
Plugged funnel—(b)
Bucket—(a)
Evaporating flask—(i)
Vase—(e)

The three remaining graphs give the following bottles:

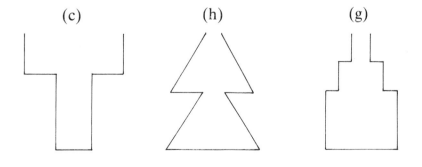

SUPPLEMENTARY BOOKLETS

The pupil's booklets which follow, provide further practice at the ideas developed in Unit A, and may be used for revision, for homework or for additional classwork.

Interpreting points continues the work introduced in A1, by providing additional material on the interpretation and use of scattergraphs. The fourth item illustrates the classic predator-prey relationship often encountered in biological work.

Sketching graphs from words extends the work introduced in A3. The introductory situation invites pupils to interpret and discuss the meaning of several sketch graphs with particular reference to the changes in gradient. This is followed by further practice at translating "full descriptions" and "trigger phrases" into sketch graphs. Pupils are also invited to invent their own situations to accompany given sketch graphs—a very demanding activity.

Sketching graphs from pictures introduces an unusual coordinate system, where each position in the plane is described by a pair of distances (x, y) from two fixed points. As pupils explore trajectories in this plane and the cartesian graphs (relating y to x) which result, they will uncover several surprising geometrical results and at the same time gain much valuable practice at sketching graphs and finding simple algebraic formulae. This booklet can be used to supplement any of the booklets in Unit A.

INTERPRETING POINTS

1. School Reports

Alex has been extremely lazy all term and this has resulted in an extremely poor examination performance

Suzy is a very able pupil, as her exam mark clearly shows, but her concentration and behaviour in the classroom are very poor. With more effort, she could do extremely well in this subject.

Catherine has worked well and deserves this marvelous examination result. Well Done!

David has worked reasonably well this term and has achieved a satisfactory examination result.

Each school report is represented by one of the points in the graph below. Label four points with the names Alex, Suzy, Catherine and David. Make up a school report for the remaining point.

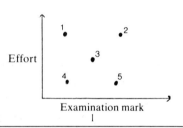

1

4. Sharks and Fish

Below is a simplified description of what can happen when two species interact. The sharks are the predators and the fish are the prey. The situation in statement A has been represented on the graph by a point.

How does this point move as time goes by?

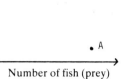

(A) Due to the absence of many sharks, there is an abundant supply of fish in the area . . .

(B) Sensing a plentiful supply of fish for food, sharks enter the area.

(C) The sharks eat many of the fish until . . .

(D) . . .the fish population is insufficient to support all the sharks. Many sharks therefore decide to leave.

(E) With few sharks around, the fish population increases once again.

(F) The area now contains enough food to support more sharks, so they return . . .

(G) and begin to eat the fish . . .until . . .

4

2. Is Height Hereditary?

In an experiment, 192 fathers and sons were measured.
(The sons were measured when they had attained their full adult height.)

* What can you say about points A and B?

* What conclusions can be drawn from this graph?

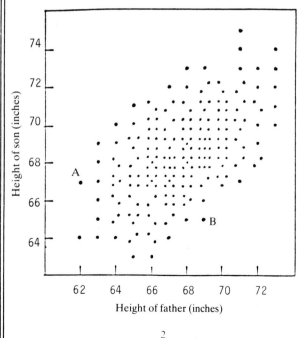

2

3. Bags of Sugar

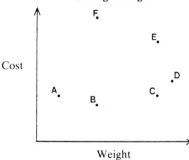

Each point on this graph represents a bag of sugar.
(a) Which bag is the heaviest?
(b) Which bag is the cheapest?
(c) Which bags are the same weight?
(d) Which bags are the same price?
(e) Which of F or C would give better value for money? How can you tell?
(f) Which of B or C would give better value for money? How can you tell?
(g) Which two bags would give the same value for money? How can you tell?

3

100

SOME SOLUTIONS

1. School reports

The graph should be labelled as illustrated below:

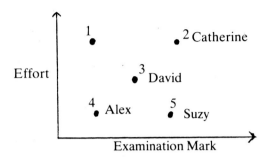

The remaining point represents someone who has worked very hard, but did not perform well in the examination.

2. Is height hereditary?

It is clear that there is some connection between the height of a father and the height of his son: A tall father is more likely to have a tall son. In this sample, no man 73 inches high has a son less than 70 inches, while no man of height 63 inches has a son as tall as 70 inches. In mathematical terms, there is a positive correlation between the two variables.

3. Bags of sugar

(a) Bag D is the heaviest.
(b) Bag B is the cheapest.
(c) Bags B and F are the same weight.
(d) Bags A and C are the same price.
(e) Bag C gives the better value for money.
(f) Bag C gives the better value for money.
(g) Bags A and F give the same value for money.

4. Sharks and fish

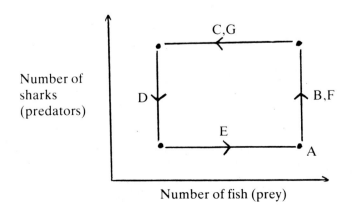

SKETCHING GRAPHS FROM WORDS

Hoisting the flag

Every morning, on the summer camp, the youngest boy scout has to hoist a flag to the top of the flagpole.

  (i) Explain in words what each of the graphs below would mean.

 (ii) Which graph shows this situation most realistically? Explain.

(iii) Which graph is the least realistic? Explain.

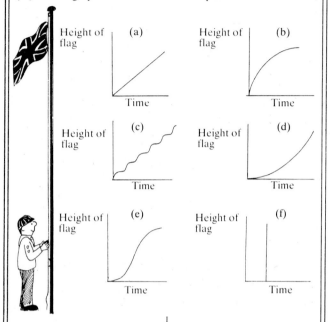

1

Sketch graphs to illustrate the following situations. *You* have to decide on the variables and the relationships involved. Label your axes carefully, and explain your graphs in words underneath.

How does . . .

1 Your height vary with age?

2 The amount of dough needed to make a pizza depend upon its diameter?

3 The amount of daylight we get depend upon the time of year?

4 The number of people in a supermarket vary during a typical Saturday?

5 The speed of a pole-vaulter vary during a typical jump?

6 The water level in your bathtub vary, before, during and after you take a bath?

4

Choose the best graph to describe each of the situations listed below. Copy the graph and label the axes clearly with the variables shown in brackets. If you cannot find the graph you want, then draw your own version and explain it fully.

1) The weightlifter held the bar over his head for a few unsteady seconds, and then with a violent crash he dropped it. (height of bar/time)

2) When I started to learn the guitar, I initially made very rapid progress. But I have found that the better you get, the more difficult it is to improve still further. (proficiency/amount of practice)

3) If schoolwork is too easy, you don't learn anything from doing it. On the other hand, if it is so difficult that you cannot understand it, again you don't learn. That is why it is so important to pitch work at the right level of difficulty. (educational value/difficulty of work)

4) When jogging, I try to start off slowly, build up to a comfortable speed and then slow down gradually as I near the end of a session. (distance/time)

5) "In general, larger animals live longer than smaller animals and their hearts beat slower. With twenty-five million heartbeats per life as a rule of thumb, we find that the rat lives for only three years, the rabbit seven and the elephant and whale even longer. As respiration is coupled with heartbeat—usually one breath is taken every four heartbeats—the rate of breathing also decreases with increasing size. (heart rate/life span)

6) As for 5, except the variables are (heart rate/breathing rate)

2

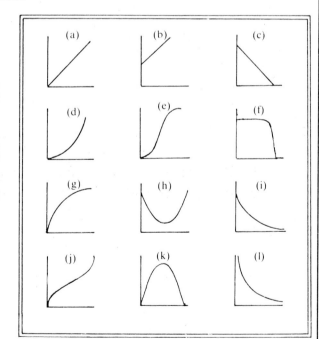

Now make up three stories of your own to accompany three of the remaining graphs. Pass your stories to your neighbour. Can they choose the correct graphs to go with the stories?

3

SOME SOLUTIONS

Page 1. Hoisting the flag

Graph (a):   would mean that the flag was being raised at a constant rate.

Graph (b):   the flag was raised quickly to start with, then gradually slowed down, near the top.

Graph (c):   the flag was hoisted in 'jerks', presumably as the scout pulled the rope 'hand over hand'.

Graph (d):   the flag was hoisted slowly to begin with, but gradually accelerated up the pole.

Graph (e):   the flag began rising slowly, then speeded up, and finally slowed down near the top of the pole.

Graph (f):   impossible! (Included for those who see the graph as a 'picture' of the situation rather than as an abstract representation of it!)

Page 2.   The situations can be paired off with the graphs as follows:

1 and (f)   (Height of bar against time)

2 and (g)   (Proficiency against amount of practice)

3 and (k)   (Educational value against difficulty of work)

4 and (e)   (Distance against time)

5 and (l)   (Heart rate against life span)

6 and (a)   (Heart rate against breathing rate).

(However, these answers must not be regarded as the only possible correct ones).

Page 4.   Suitable sketch graphs for the six items are:

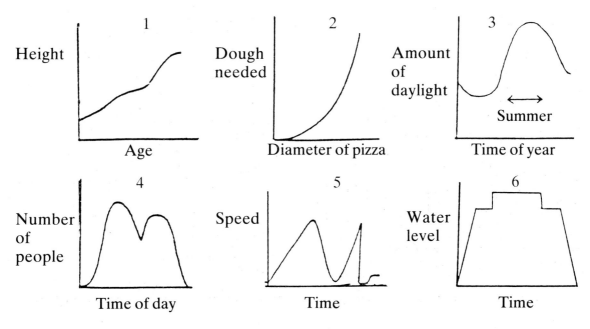

103

SKETCHING GRAPHS FROM PICTURES
Particles and Paths

In the diagram above, there are 5 particles labelled p, q, r, s and t.

* Without measuring, can you label each point on the graph below with the correct letter?

Now *check* your answer by measurement
(A and B are 6 cm apart)

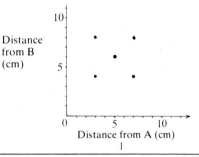

Distance from B (cm)

Distance from A (cm)

1

In the accompanying booklet, particles are moving along a number of different paths.

For each situation:

* Sketch a rough graph to show how the distance from B will vary with the distance from A.

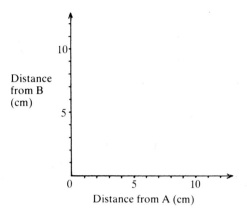

Distance from B (cm)

Distance from A (cm)

* *Check* your answer by measuring various positions, recording your answers in a table and by *plotting* a few points accurately.

* Try to find a formula which describes the relationship between the two distances.

Continue exploring other paths and their graphs.

Write up all your findings.

4

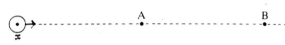

In this diagram, particle x is moving slowly along the path shown by the dotted line, from left to right.

* Sketch a graph to show how the distance from B relates to the distance from A during this motion.

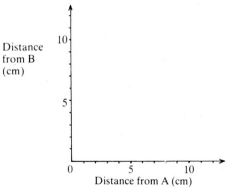

Distance from B (cm)

Distance from A (cm)

* Check your answer by measuring various positions and recording them in the table:

Distance from A (cm)	6	5	4	3	2	1	0	1	2
Distance from B (cm)	12								

Write down any formulae that you can find which fit your graph.

2

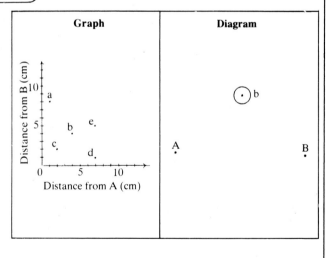

Try to mark the positions of the five particles a, b, c, d and e on the right hand diagram (b has been done for you).

* Which positions are impossible to mark? Why is this? Try to mark other points on the graph which would give impossible positions on the diagram. Shade in these forbidden regions on the graph.

* One position of particle b has been shown. Is this the only position which is 4 cm from both A and B? Mark in any other possible positions for particle b.

* Which points on the graph give *only one* possible position on the diagram?

3

104

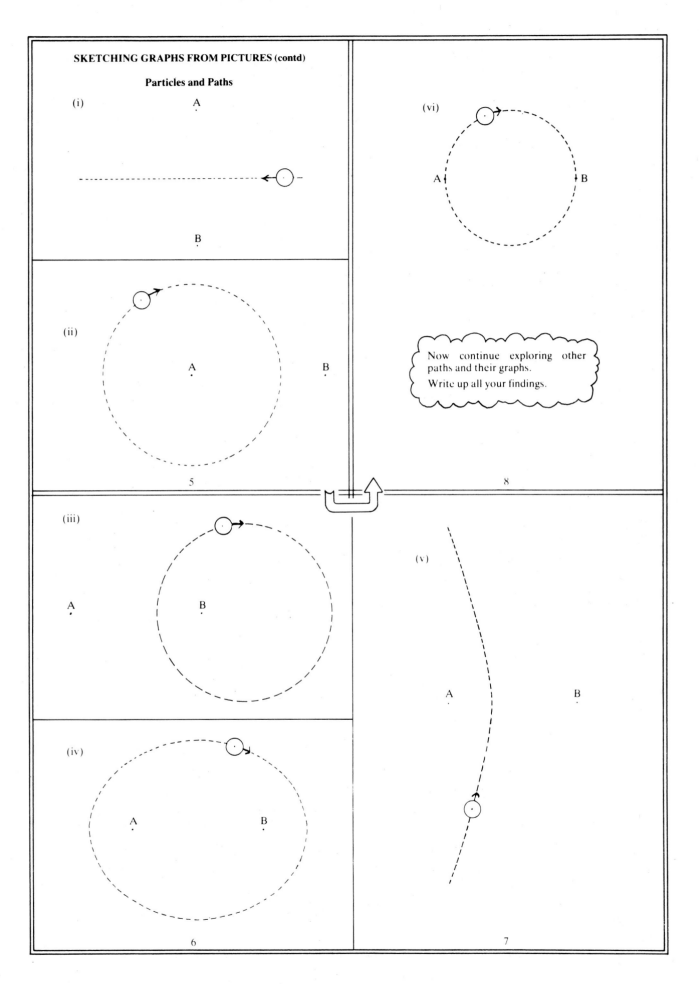

SKETCHING GRAPHS FROM PICTURES (contd)

Particles and Paths

(i)

(ii)

5

(iii)

(iv)

6

(vi)

Now continue exploring other paths and their graphs.

Write up all your findings.

8

(v)

7

Page 1.

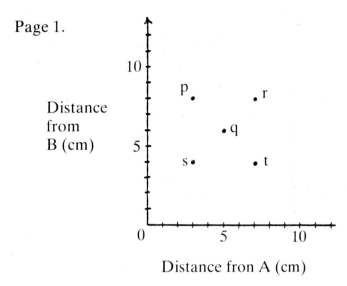

Page 2.

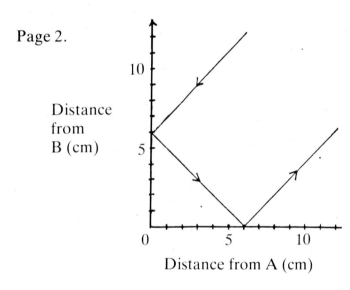

The arrows indicate the direction of travel of the particle. So, for the first part of the motion (until the particle reaches A):
$y = x + 6$,
from A to B:
$x + y = 6$
and from B onwards:
$y = x - 6$
where x and y are the distances from A and B respectively.

Page 3.

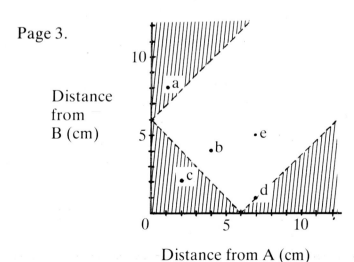

All the points in the shaded region are impossible to mark on the diagram.

The points which lie on the boundary line are the only points which give one possible position on the diagram.

Page 4 and the second booklet:

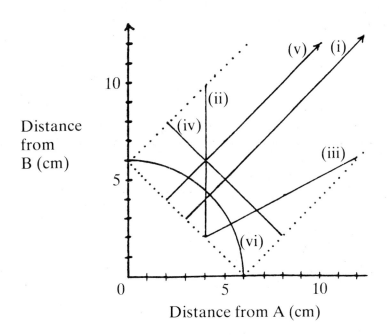

Each of these graphs must lie within the boundary indicated by the dotted line.

Their equations are:

(i) $y = x$ $(x \geqslant 3)$
(ii) $x = 4$ $(2 \leqslant y \leqslant 10)$
(iii) $y = \frac{1}{2}x$ $(4 \leqslant x \leqslant 12)$
(iv) $x + y = 10$ $(2 \leqslant x \leqslant 8)$
(v) $y = x + 2$ $(x \geqslant 2)$
(vi) $x^2 + y^2 = 36$ $(x \geqslant 0, y \geqslant 0)$

Unit B

CONTENTS

INTRODUCTION

In this Unit we offer pupils the opportunity to discover and explore patterns and functions arising from realistic situations and relate these to algebraic expressions which include linear, reciprocal, quadratic and exponential functions.

This Unit contains four lesson outlines, and is intended to occupy approximately two weeks.

B1 contains a collection of activities which are designed to involve pupils in translating directly between tables of data and sketch graphs. By freeing them from time consuming technical skills (plotting points etc), pupils are encouraged to look at tables in a more global and qualitative manner.

B2 attempts to involve pupils in searching for functions in situations. Pupils are invited to sketch graphs, construct tables of values and find formulae wherever possible.

B3 involves the explorations of exponential functions within the context of "Hypnotic drugs". We have included this activity because many textbooks appear to neglect these important functions. This is perhaps due to the fact that their study usually involves a great deal of difficult computation. However, with the advent of the calculator, exponential functions can be investigated by everyone.

B4 presents a situation where three independent variables are involved. The pupil's booklet offers a collection of unsorted data concerning the strength of various 'bridges' with different dimensions. By holding two dimensions constant (length and thickness for example) a relationship can be discovered between the third (breadth) and the maximum weight the bridge will support. If pupils organise their attack on this problem in this way, they may discover a law by which the strength of any bridge may be predicted.

To conclude this Unit, we again offer some further activities which may be used to supplement these materials. These include more algebraic material.

B1 SKETCHING GRAPHS FROM TABLES

In this booklet, you will be asked to explore several tables of data, and attempt to discover any patterns or trends that they contain.

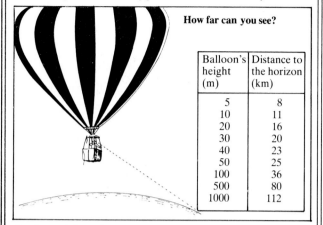

How far can you see?

Balloon's height (m)	Distance to the horizon (km)
5	8
10	11
20	16
30	20
40	23
50	25
100	36
500	80
1000	112

Look carefully at the table shown above.

* Without accurately plotting the points, try to sketch a rough graph to describe the relationship between the balloon's height, and the distance to the horizon.

Distance to the horizon / Balloon's height

Explain your method for doing this.

1

Try to *make up* tables of numbers which will correspond to the following six graphs: (They do not need to represent real situations).

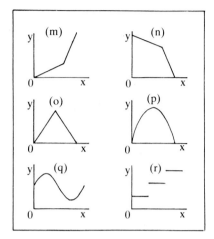

Now make up some tables of your own, and sketch the corresponding graphs on a separate sheet of paper. (Again they do not need to represent real situations). Pass only *the tables* to your neighbour.
She must now try to sketch graphs from your tables. Compare her solutions with yours.

4

Without plotting, choose the best sketch graph (from the selection on page 3) to fit each of the tables shown below. Particular graphs may fit more than one table. Copy the most suitable graph, name the axes clearly, and explain your choice. If you cannot find the graph you want, draw your own version.

1. Cooling Coffee

Time (minutes)	0	5	10	15	20	25	30
Temperature (C°)	90	79	70	62	55	49	44

2. Cooking Times for Turkey

Weight (lb)	6	8	10	12	14	16	18	20
Time (hours)	2½	3	3½	4	4½	5	5½	6

3. How a Baby Grew Before Birth

Age (months)	2	3	4	5	6	7	8	9
Length (cm)	4	9	16	24	30	34	38	42

4. After Three Pints of Beer ...

Time (hours)	1	2	3	4	5	6	7
Alcohol in the blood (mg/100ml)	90	75	60	45	30	15	0

5. Number of Bird Species on a Volcanic Island

Year	1880	1890	1900	1910	1920	1930	1940
Number of Species	0	1	5	17	30	30	30

6. Life Expectancy

Age (years)	Number of Survivors	Age (years)	Number of Survivors
0	1000	50	913
5	979	60	808
10	978	70	579
20	972	80	248
30	963	90	32
40	950	100	1

2

(a) (b) (c) (d)

(e) (f) (g) (h)

(i) (j) (k) (l)

Without plotting, try and sketch a graph to illustrate the following table:

How daylight summer temperature varies as you go higher in the atmosphere

Altitude (km)	Temperature (°C)	Altitude (km)	Temperature (°C)
0	20	60	−12
10	−48	70	−56
20	−50	80	−80
30	−38	90	−90
40	−18	100	−75
50	6	110	−20

3

B1. (contd)   SOME HINTS ON SKETCHING GRAPHS FROM TABLES

Look again at the balloon problem, "How far can you see?"

The following discussion should help you to see how you can go about sketching quick graphs from tables without having to spend a long time plotting points.

*   As the balloon's height increases by *equal* amounts, what happens to the 'distance to the horizon'? Does it increase or decrease?

Balloon's height (m)	5	10	20	30	40	50	100	500	1000
Distance to horizon (km)	8	11	16	20	23	25	36	80	112

Does this distance
increase by equal amounts? . . .

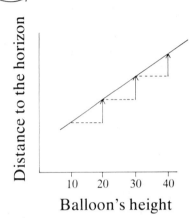
Balloon's height

. . .or increase by greater
and greater amounts? . . .

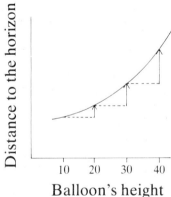
Balloon's height

. . .or increase by smaller and
smaller amounts?

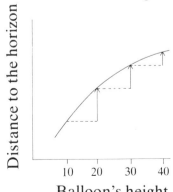
Balloon's height

Now ask yourself:
● do the other numbers in the table
  fit in with this overall trend?
● will the graph cross the axes?
  If so, where?

111

B1.   SKETCHING GRAPHS FROM TABLES

In this lesson, pupils are invited to explore tables of data and attempt to describe the patterns and trends they observe using sketch graphs. By freeing pupils from time consuming technical skills, such as deciding on scales and accurate point plotting, we aim to enable pupils to look at tables in a more global, qualitative manner. Between one and two hours will be needed.

Suggested Presentation

1. Issue the booklet and allow the pupils time to work on the balloon problem, "How far can you see?", in pairs or small groups. Encourage each group to try to agree on a correct sketch graph, and ask them to write down an explanation of their method.

2. Tour the room, listening and asking pupils to explain what they are doing. In spite of the instructions in the booklet, a few pupils may still feel an irresistible urge to plot accurate points. Discourage this, by asking them to try to describe how the numbers are changing in words, and inviting them to translate this verbal description into a sketch graph.

3. After giving them time to attempt the problem, hold a short class discussion to discover their different approaches. Then give each pupil a copy of the follow-up sheet "Some hints on sketching graphs from tables". This sheet describes one way of sketching a quick graph, by examining differences between entries in the table. Discuss this sheet with the class, emphasising the value of incrementing the balloon's height by *equal* amounts in order to find the overall shape of the graph. The final questions on the sheet may cause some disagreement. When deciding where the graph meets the axes, some may reason that when the balloon is on the ground, the distance the pilot can see is not zero. Others may decide that the "balloon's height" is equivalent to "the height of the pilot's eye above the ground" in which case the graph will pass through the origin. It is not important that such issues are resolved however, so long as pupils clearly understand how the graphs relate to *their* interpretations of the situation.

4. Now ask the pupils to continue working through the booklet, discussing each item in pairs or small groups. Emphasise the importance of labelling axes and writing explanations when matching the tables to the graphs on pages 2 and 3. As pupils work through these items they may realise that different sketch graphs may be made to fit a particular table if the axes are labelled differently. For example, for item 3, "How a baby grew before birth", *both* of the graphs shown below are valid solutions:

112

Considerable argument may also be generated when discussing if or where the graph should meet the axes. For example, some pupils may reject graph (b) in favour of graph (a) for the "Cooking times for Turkey" item, because they reason that "the graph *must* pass through the origin because a bird with zero weight will take no time to cook". (This is a particular case where *none* of the suggested sketch graphs fit the situation perfectly!) The final item on page 3 asks pupils to sketch a graph to illustrate a table which describes how the temperature of the atmosphere varies with altitude. In this case, some pupils may find it difficult to decide whether a change from $-48°C$ to $-50°C$ is a rise or fall in temperature and may need help when examining the differences between successive table entries.

5. The first item on Page 4 of the booklet invites pupils to construct their own tables of data, corresponding to six given graphs. This is a fairly open-ended activity with many correct solutions. As well as deciding whether the entries in a table should increase or decrease, pupils will need to decide exactly *how* the numbers increase or decrease. In particular, a comparison of graphs (o), (p) and (q) should provoke a useful discussion on gradients. The remaining item requires each pupil to first invent their own table of data, and then compare their sketch graph solution with one drawn by their neighbour. This kind of feedback provides pupils with a way of assessing their own understanding and usually generates a useful group discussion.

B1.   SOME SOLUTIONS

Page 1:   How far can you see?

The sketch graph should look something like the following:

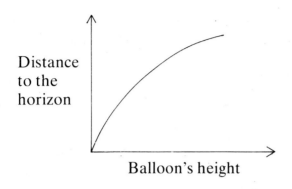

Distance to the horizon

Balloon's height

Page 2:   The tables can be paired off with the graphs as follows:

> '1. Cooling coffee' with graph (g)
>
> '2. Cooking times for turkey' with graph (b)
>
> '3. How a baby grew before birth' with graph (i)
>
> '4. After three pints of beer . . .' with graph (e)
>
> '5. Number of bird species on a volcanic island' with graph (k)
>
> '6. Life expectancy' with graph (l)

(In each of the above cases, the independent variable has been identified with the horizontal axis.)

However, in giving these answers, we are aware that, in several cases, these graphs do not correspond to the situations very closely. For example, the graph for item 2, 'Cooking times for turkey', is unrealistic for very small turkey weights. It implies, for example, that a turkey with zero weight will still take one hour to cook! Pupils may therefore prefer to choose graph (i):

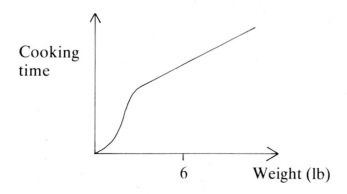

Cooking time

6   Weight (lb)

114

Page 3: How temperature varies with altitude

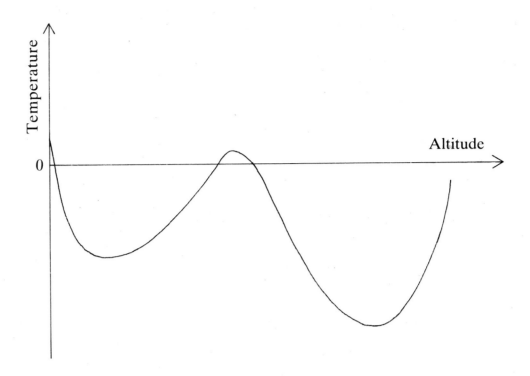

The shape of this graph may surprise you. Contrary to popular belief, atmospheric temperature does not drop steadily as altitude increases. It does fall from ground level to the top of the "Troposphere", but in the "Stratosphere" it rises—affected by ozone (a heat-absorbing form of oxygen). In the ozone-free "Mesosphere" the air cools, while in the "Thermosphere" it rises again.

B2 FINDING FUNCTIONS IN SITUATIONS

The Rabbit Run

Length

A rectangular rabbit run is to be made from 22 metres of wire fencing. The owner is interested in knowing how the area enclosed by the fence will depend upon the length of the run.

Think carefully about this situation, and discuss it with your neighbour.

* Describe, in writing, how the enclosed area will change as the length increases through *all* possible values.
* Illustrate your answer using a sketch graph:

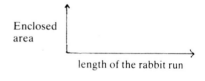

Enclosed area

length of the rabbit run

1

For each of the two situations which follow,

(i) Describe your answer by *sketching* a rough graph.
(ii) Explain the shape of your graph in words.
(iii) Check your graph by constructing a table of values, and redraw it if necessary.
(iv) Try to find an algebraic formula.

The Outing

A coach hire firm offers to loan a luxury coach for £120 per day. The organiser of the trip decides to charge every member of the party an equal amount for the ride.
How will the size of each person's contribution depend upon the size of the party?

Developing Photographs

"Happy Snaps" photographic service offer to develop your film for £1 (a fixed price for processing) plus 10p for each print. How does the cost of developing a film vary with the number of prints you want developed?

4

The pupils shown below have all attempted this problem. Comment on their answers, and try to explain their mistakes.

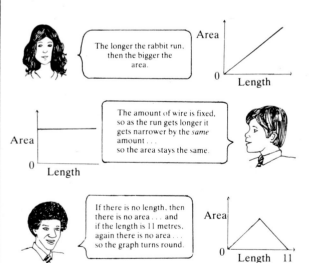

The longer the rabbit run, then the bigger the area.

Area / Length

The amount of wire is fixed, so as the run gets longer it gets narrower by the *same* amount . . . so the area stays the same.

Area / Length

If there is no length, then there is no area . . . and if the length is 11 metres, again there is no area . . . so the graph turns round.

Area / Length 11

Longer runs are narrower, so the area drops.

Area / Length

2

* In order to see how good your sketch is, construct a table of values:

Length of run (metres)											
Area (square metres)											

* Do you notice any patterns in this table?
  Write down what they are and try to explain *why* they occur.

* Now, redraw your sketch using the patterns you have observed. (This does not need to be done accurately).

* Using your sketch and your table of values, find out what the dimensions of the boundary should be to obtain the greatest possible space for the rabbit to move around in.

* Finally, try to find an algebraic formula which fits this situation.

3

116

In this lesson, we invite pupils to explore several situations in order to discover the functions (quadratic, reciprocal and linear) which underlie them. The situations are presented verbally, and pupils are initially asked to describe the relationships by sketching (not plotting) rough graphs and writing explanations. In this way, we hope that they will achieve a qualitative 'feel' for the nature of the functions. Pupils are then asked to check their sketch graphs by constructing and observing trends and patterns contained in tables of values, (using the methods introduced in B1). Finally, we challenge the pupils to try to describe the functions using formulae. (Notice how this completely inverts the traditional formula → table → graph sequence.) Between one and two hours will be needed.

Suggested Presentation

1. Issue the booklet and introduce the 'Rabbit run' problem to the class. It is quite helpful to use a loop of string and enlist the help of two pupils to illustrate how the shape of the rabbit run changes as the length of the run is increased:

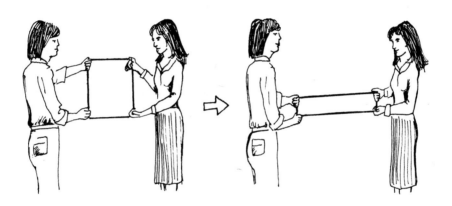

Some pupils assume that the word 'length' means 'the longest dimension'. Explain that this is not the case, and that in this problem the length can even be made to take very small values.

2. Now invite the pupils to discuss the relationship between the enclosed area and the length of the rabbit run in pairs or small groups. Ask each group to produce one sketch graph which adequately describes the situation, together with a written explanation, as suggested in the booklet. Emphasise that only a *sketch* graph is needed, it does not need to be drawn accurately.

3. After giving them adequate time to do this, you may decide to collect together some of their ideas on the blackboard and hold a class discussion concerning the thought processes that went into these attempts. Again, we recommend that you act more as a 'chairman' or 'devil's advocate' than as a 'judge' at this stage (as described on the inside back cover of this book). You may be quite surprised at the variety of responses that are received. Page 2 of the pupil's booklet illustrates

four typical graphs and explanations. In addition, pupils often think a great deal about the practicalities of the situation, (for example the problem of putting a hutch inside a very narrow enclosure), and often argue that "the enclosed area can never become zero, or the rabbit would be squashed!" They therefore reason that the graph should never cross the horizontal axis. Whether or not you decide to hold a class discussion, we recommend that all pupils are given an opportunity to write down their criticisms of the four solutions presented on page 2 of the pupil's booklet. Such an exercise requires a great deal of thought and explanation.

4. Pupils should now be encouraged to check their sketches by completing the table of data as shown on page 3 of the booklet:

Length of run (metres)	0	1	2	3	4	5	6	7	8	9	10	11
Area (square metres)	0	10	18	24	28	30	30	28	24	18	10	0

Again discourage them from plotting all these points, unless this is absolutely necessary. Instead, remind them of the methods they used to sketch graphs from tables in the previous booklet (B1). Some pupils may reason that the maximum possible area occurs when the run is "5 or 6 metres" in length. Remind them of their initial sketch graph, (which probably didn't have a plateau), and if this still does not help, ask them to consider non-integral values of the length.

5. Finding the final algebraic formula for this situation will provide a stumbling block for many pupils. It often helps if they are first asked to speak and *then* write down a *verbal* recipe for finding the enclosed area for any given length of the rabbit run. For example:

    "Double the length, and take this away from 22 metres to find out how much is left for the two widths. Halve this to find the size of each width. Now multiply this by the length for the area."

    This may then be translated into $(22 - 2L) \times \frac{1}{2} \times L = A$.

6. The final two situations may now be attempted. The first situation produces a rectangular hyperbola, and the second, a straight line. Considerable argument may be generated as pupils try to decide if and where the graphs should cross the axes. (For example, in the second situation, "If you have no prints developed, it won't cost anything." "Can you have a film processed without having any prints?" etc.).

7. In the supplementary section to this Unit, (see page 131), we have included some further situations which may be explored in a similar manner. These may be used as a resource for further practice or for homework.

B2 SOME SOLUTIONS

The Rabbit Run

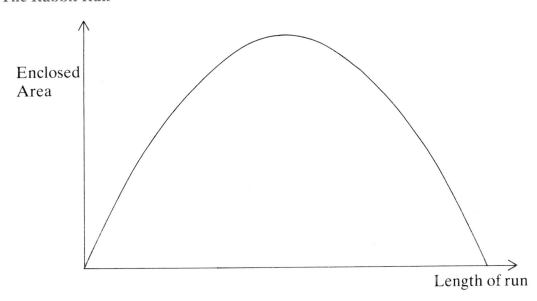

Length of run (metres)	0	1	2	3	4	5	6	7	8	9	10	11
Enclosed Area (m²)	0	10	18	24	28	30	30	28	24	18	10	0

$A = L(11 - L)$ where A square metres = enclosed area
L metres = Length of rabbit run.

The maximum area occurs when the shape of the boundary is a square, with each side measuring 5½ metres.

The Outing

This produces the formula $C = \dfrac{120}{N}$, where £C = size of each contribution
N = number of people in party.

Developing Photographs

This produces the formula $C = 10N + 100$, where C pence = cost of developing a film
N = number of prints required.

B3 LOOKING AT EXPONENTIAL FUNCTIONS

Hypnotic Drugs

Sometimes, doctors prescribe 'hypnotic drugs' (e.g. sleeping pills) to patients who, either through physical pain or emotional tension, find that they cannot sleep. (Others are used as mild sedatives or for anaesthetics during operations). There are many different kinds of drugs which can be prescribed. One important requirement is that the effect of the drug should wear off by the following morning, otherwise the patient will find himself drowsy all through the next day. This could be dangerous if, for example, he has to drive to work! Of course, for someone confined to a hospital bed this wouldn't matter so much.

1

Imagine that a doctor prescribed a drug called Triazolam. (Halcion®).

After taking some pills, the drug eventually reaches a level* of 4μg/l in the blood plasma.

How quickly will the drug wear off?

Look at the table shown below:

Drug name (and Brand name)	Approximate formula
Triazolam (Halcion®)	$y = A \times (0.84)^x$
Nitrazepam (Mogadon®)	$y = A \times (0.97)^x$
Pentobombitone (Sonitan®)	$y = A \times (1.15)^x$
Methohexitone (Brietal®)	$y = A \times (0.5)^x$
KEY A = size of the initial dose in the blood	
y = amount of drug in the blood	
x = time in hours after the drug reaches the blood.	

For Triazolam, the formula is $y = A \times (0.84)^x$

In our problem the initial dose is 4 μg/l, so this becomes
$$y = 4 \times (0.84)^x$$

---

* Please note that in this worksheet, doses and blood concentrations are not the same as those used in clinical practice, and the formulae may vary coniderably owing to physiological differences between patients.

2

---

* Check your sketch graphs by plotting *a few* points accurately on graph paper. Share this work out with your neighbour so that it doesn't take too long.

* Do just *one* of the two investigations shown below:

> Draw an accurate graph to show how the effect of Triazolam wears off.
>
> After how many hours has the amount of drug in the blood halved?
>
> How does this "Half life" depend on the size of the initial dose?
>
> Write down and explain your findings.

> Investigate the effect of taking a 4μg dose of Methohexitone every hour.
>
> Draw an accurate graph and write about its implications.

4

---

* Continue the table below, using a calculator, to show how the drug wears off during the first 10 hours.
  You do not need to plot a graph.

Time (hours)	Amount of drug left in the blood
x	y
0	4
1	3.36 (= 4 × 0.84)
2	2.82 (= 3.36 × 0.84)
.	.
.	.
.	.

* Which of the following graphs best describes your data? Explain how you can tell *without plotting*

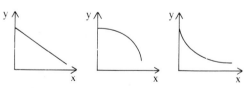

* *On the same pair of axes*, sketch four graphs to compare how a 4μg dose* of each of the drugs will wear off.
  (*Guess* the graphs—*do not* draw them accurately)

* Only three of the drugs are real. The other was intended as a joke! Which is it? Explain how you can tell.
  What would happen if you took this drug?

3

120

This booklet provides a practical context within which the properties of exponential functions may be discussed. Pupils will need to have access to calculators so that they can avoid becoming bogged down in unnecessary arithmetic. Graph paper will also be needed for the final two investigations on page 4 of the booklet. Between one and two hours will be needed.

Suggested Presentation

1. Although the booklet alone may be used to introduce the situation, it is probably much better to discuss the first two pages with the class. The formulae which occur on the second page may appear daunting to some pupils, and it is therefore advisable to go through the "Triazolam" example with them.

   In particular, discuss various ways of using a calculator to find the amount of Triazolam in the blood (y) after successive hours (x), from the formula:

   $$y = 4 \times (0.84)^x$$

   The most obvious key sequence is:

   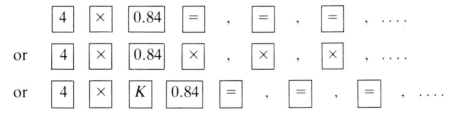

   but there are considerable advantages in using a 'constant' multiplying facility if one is available:

   Although different calculators perform this function in different ways, we feel that it is important to discuss this issue so that pupils become fluent in the operation of their own machines. Of course, the amount of drug in the blood, after say 5 hours, can be evaluated more directly using the $\boxed{x^y}$ button if this is available.

   e.g. $\boxed{4}$ $\boxed{\times}$ $\boxed{0.84}$ $\boxed{x^y}$ $\boxed{5}$ $\boxed{=}$

2. Some pupils may appear surprised that repeatedly multiplying can actually *decrease* a quantity. From their earliest experiences with whole numbers, multiplication was always viewed as 'repeated addition', and it therefore always 'made things bigger'. This misconception is extremely common, and it is therefore worth discussing in some depth.

3. Now allow the pupils to continue working on the booklet in pairs or small groups. On the final page of the booklet, encourage the pupils to share the work

out between them. For example, they may each choose to do a different investigation, and then report on their findings to the other members of the group.

Finally, encourage pupils to write up all their discoveries.

4. To conclude the lesson, you may like to generalise the work in the booklet by discussion concerning the shape of $y = 4a^x$, $(a > 0)$.

    For example, the following questions are very searching, and can lead to some deep, invaluable discussions.

    "How can you tell, purely by inspection, whether the function is increasing or decreasing?"

    "Is y always greater than zero? Why?"

    "What does a mean when x is *not* a whole number? a^2 means $a \times a$, but you cannot multiply a by itself 'half' a time or 'minus three' times . . .can you?"

    "What would happen if $a < 0$?"

B3   SOME SOLUTIONS

The following sketch graph shows roughly how the same dose of each drug will wear off.

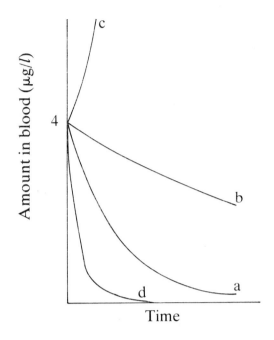

Key:
a = Triazolam
b = Nitrazepam
c = Pentobombitone
d = Methohexitone

(Immediately, we can see that Pentobombitone was the joke drug.)

The first of the final investigations should lead to the following two conclusions:
— the half life of Triazolam ≈ 4 hours
— this half life is independent of the initial dose.

The second investigation asks pupils to investigate the effect of taking a 4 µg dose of Methohexitone *every hour*. This will produce the following graph, assuming that the drug enters the blood almost instantaneously:

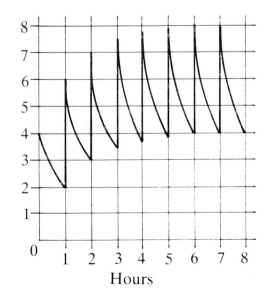

It can be seen from this graph that the maximum level of drug in the body tends towards a limiting value of 8 μg/*l*.

It is vital for doctors to know exactly how the effect of a drug will build up in the body; too much may be dangerous, and too little may be ineffective. They must therefore try to keep the oscillations in between these two boundaries. (For example, in order to reduce the size of the oscillations a doctor may prescribe that a smaller dose should be taken more frequently.)

In general, suppose that a dose of size "*d*" is administered every hour. Then the amount of drug in the blood just *before* the second dose will be *ad* (for some *a* < 1), and just after this dose, it will be *ad* + *d*.

Eventually, the quantity of drug eliminated from the blood during one hour will become equal to the size of each dose, and the drug level in the blood will then reach its maximum value, *d*max.

where $d_{max} = a \; d_{max} + d$ (see the diagram below)

and so $d_{max} = \dfrac{d}{1 - a}$

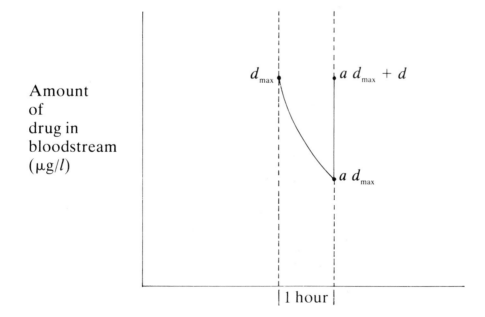

Alternatively, after successive hours, the maximum amount of drug in the blood will be:

$$d, \; d(1+a), \; d(1+a+a^2), \; d(1+a+a^2+a^3) \ldots \frac{d(1-a^{n+1})}{1-a}$$

and as $n \to \infty$, this approaches $\dfrac{d}{1-a}$, since $a < 1$.

B4 A FUNCTION WITH SEVERAL VARIABLES

In this booklet you will be considering the following problem:

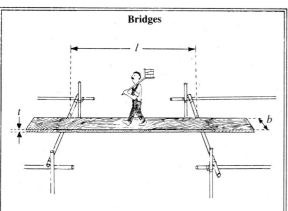

Bridges

How can you predict whether a plank bridge will collapse under the weight of the person crossing it?

* Imagine the distance between the bridge supports (*l*) being slowly changed. How will this affect the maximum weight (*w*) that can safely go across?

Sketch a graph to show how *w* will vary with *l*.

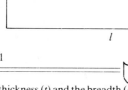

1

At the moment, we have 3 variables; length, breadth, and thickness. If we keep two of these variables *fixed*, then we may be able to discover a relationship between the third variable and the weight the plank will support.

So...

* Collect together all the data which relates to a plank with breadth 30 cm and thickness 2 cm, and make a table:

Length of plank (*l* metres)				
Maximum weight supported (*w* kg wt)				

Describe any patterns or rules that you spot. (Can you predict, for example, the value of *w* when $l = 6$?)
Does your sketch graph agree with this table?
Try to write down a formula to fit this data.

* Now look at all bridges with a fixed length and breadth, and try to find a connection between the thickness and the maximum weight it will support.
Describe what you discover, as before.

* Now look at all planks with a fixed length and thickness.

For geniuses only! Can you combine *all* your results to obtain a formula which can be used to predict the strength of a bridge with *any* dimensions?

* Finally, what will happen in this situation?

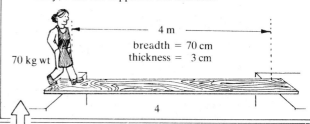

70 kg wt

4 m
breadth = 70 cm
thickness = 3 cm

4

---

* Now imagine that, in turn, the thickness (*t*) and the breadth (*b*) of the bridge are changed. Sketch two graphs to show the effect on *w*.

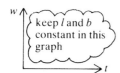 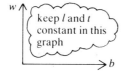

keep *l* and *b* constant in this graph

keep *l* and *t* constant in this graph

* Compare your graphs with those drawn by your neighbour. Try to convince her that your graphs are correct. It does not matter too much if you cannot agree at this stage.

* Write down an explanation for the shape of each of your graphs.

The table on the next page shows the maximum weights that can cross bridges with different dimensions. The results are written in order, from the strongest bridge to the weakest.

* Try to discover patterns or rules by which the strength of a bridge can be *predicted* from its dimensions.

Some Hints: Try reorganising this table, so that *l*, *b* and *t* vary in a systematic way.

Try keeping *b* and *t* fixed, and look at how *w* depends on *l*...

If you are still stuck, then there are more hints on page 4.

2

Distance between supports *l*(m)	Breadth *b*(cm)	Thickness *t*(cm)	Maximum supportable weight *w*(kg wt)
2	40	5	250
1	20	5	250
2	50	4	200
2	40	4	160
1	20	4	160
2	20	5	125
2	30	4	120
1	20	3	90
2	20	4	80
1	30	2	60
4	40	3	45
1	20	2	40
2	10	4	40
2	30	2	30
3	30	2	20
3	10	3	15
4	30	2	15
5	30	2	12
1	20	1	10
4	40	1	5

3

126

This booklet provides an opportunity for pupils to discover an underlying pattern in a table of unsorted data. Since three independent variables are involved (breadth, length and thickness) this will require an appreciation that two need to be held constant in order to find a relationship between the third variable and the strength of the plank. The relationships involved are linear, reciprocal and quadratic respectively and should therefore be within the experience of most pupils. The microcomputer program, "Bridges", (provided within the support material to this module) considerably enhances this presentation. Between one and two hours will be needed.

Suggested Presentation

1.   Issue the booklet and allow the class sufficient time to sketch and discuss three sketch graphs relating the length, breadth and thickness of the plank to the maximum weight that it can support. (You may also decide to hold a class discussion to share their ideas). Opinions may vary widely. For example:

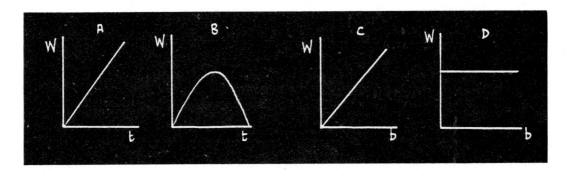

Pupil A: "Thicker bridges are stronger."

Pupil B: "No they're not, because very heavy planks have more of their own weight to support. This means that they get weaker, like graph B."

Pupil C: "Wider bridges are stronger."

Pupil D: "If the plank gets wider then it will not affect how much it will hold until you get it very wide and the weight is spread more."

At this stage the discussion need not be resolved and, in any case, it is almost impossible to form a conclusion on the little information that has been presented. The aim of this discussion is mainly to gain the interest of the pupils in the situation and enable them to think about the three variables on a global level before they become immersed in the detailed analysis of data. The sketch graphs will be referred to again, later on.

2.   After most pupils have acquired a 'feel' for this situation, allow them plenty of time to attempt to discover a rule by which the 'strength' of *any* bridge can be predicted from its dimensions using the table of data given on the third page of the booklet. The most effective method involves keeping two variables constant and discovering how the maximum supportable weight is affected by changing the third variable. A hint to this effect appears at the bottom of page 2 of the

booklet. Discourage pupils from turning to page 4 of the booklet, where more detailed guidance is to be found, until they have explored *their own* strategies for solving the problem. This will take time, and it is unwise to hurry pupils, as it is only by trying various strategies and failing that the power of a systematic approach will become apparent. However, if pupils are becoming discouraged, then tell them to read on.

3. Towards the end of the lesson, it may be worthwhile spending some time discussing any observations or rules that members of the class have discovered. If the approach outlined in the booklet is followed, then some pupils may have discovered that the maximum supportable weight is proportional to the breadth, to the square of the thickness and inversely proportional to the distance between the bridge supports. (These results can be compared with the original sketch graphs).

In fact,

when $l = 2$ and $t = 4$ then $w = 4b$ (some may have $w = b \times t$)

when $l = 1$ and $b = 20$ then $w = 10t^2$

when $b = 30$ and $t = 2$ then $w = \dfrac{60}{l}$ (some may have $w = \dfrac{b \times t}{l}$)

In order to predict the strength of any bridge, these three expressions need to be combined into one:

$$w = \frac{kbt^2}{l} \quad \text{(where } k \text{ is a constant).}$$

(By substituting values for b, t, l and w, it can be seen that $k = \frac{1}{2}$).

This final idea is very demanding, and is probably only within the reach of a very few most able pupils. Do not feel it necessary to make everyone reach this stage.

B4 SOME SOLUTIONS

The three sketch graphs should show that

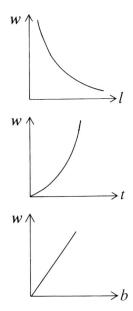

"Longer bridges are weaker"

"Thicker bridges are stronger"
(If you double the thickness, you more than
double the maximum supportable weight).

"Wider bridges are stronger"
(The fact that this relationship is linear can be
deduced by recognising that two identical planks
placed side by side will be able to support twice
as much weight as a single plank.)

Examining the large table on page 3 systematically, the following data can be
extracted:

Length of plank (*l* metres)	1	2	3	4	5	(breadth = 30 cm)
Maximum supportable weight (*w* kg wt)	60	30	20	15	12	(thickness = 2 cm)

Thickness of plank (*t* cm)	1	2	3	4	5	(length = 1 m)
Maximum supportable weight (*w* kg wt)	10	40	90	160	250	(breadth = 20 cm)

Breadth of plank (*b* cm)	10	20	30	40	50	(length = 2 m)
Maximum supportable weight (*w* kg wt)	40	80	120	160	200	(thickness = 4 cm)

From these tables the relationships $w = \dfrac{60}{l}$, $w = 4b$ and $w = 10t^2$ may be deduced.

Combining these we obtain: $w = \dfrac{bt^2}{l} \times \text{constant}$

and substituting values for b, t, l and w into this equation we find that:

$$w = \frac{bt^2}{2l}$$

Finally, according to this formula, the safe weight limit for the bridge on page 4 is
78.75 kg wt, so the woman can cross safely over.

129

SUPPLEMENTARY BOOKLETS

The pupil's booklets which follow provide additional material which give further practice and extend the ideas presented in Unit B.

Finding functions in situations. This booklet continues the work contained in B2. Six situations are presented, and pupils are invited to sketch graphs, construct tables of values and, finally, find algebraic formulae. (The functions involved are linear, quadratic, exponential and reciprocal.) Finding a formula will prove to be the major stumbling block, and it may help a great deal if pupils are first asked to *speak* and then write down in *words* the method they used for constructing the tables of values. This verbal description may then be translated into algebraic form, as described in B2. For some pupils, the algebraic part of the questions may prove to be too difficult, but they can still learn a great deal from the graph sketching and tabulating if this part is omitted.

Finding functions in tables of data. This booklet extends the work begun in B1, by introducing activities which involve fitting algebraic formulae to tables of data. Beginning with a table, pupils are asked to sketch rough graphs to illustrate the data, and match their sketch with a "Rogues gallery" of standard functions. These functions may then be made to fit the data using trial and error with a calculator, or by a little algebraic manipulation. Finally, pupils are asked to *use* their functions to produce additional data. Again, this is a demanding activity, but pupils should find it well worth the effort.

FINDING FUNCTIONS IN SITUATIONS

For each of the four situations which follow,

(i) Describe your answer by *sketching* a rough graph.

(ii) Explain the shape of your graph in words.

(iii) Check your graph by constructing a table of values, and redraw it if necessary.

(iv) If you can, try to find an algebraic formula, but do not worry too much if this proves difficult.

1 Renting a Television

A TV rental company charge £10 per month for a colour set. An introductory offer allows you to have the set rent-free for the first month. How will the total cost change as the rental period increases?

2 The Depreciating Car

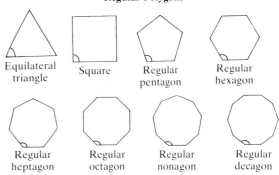

When it was new, my car cost me £3,000. Its value is depreciating at a rate of 20% per year. This means that after one year its value was

£3,000 × 0.8 = £2,400

and after two years, its value was

£2,400 × 0.8 = £1,920 and so on.

How does its value continue to change?

1

The instructions on what to do for these two questions are at the top of page 1.

3 Staircases

"The normal pace length is 60 cm. This must be decreased by 2 cm for every 1 cm that the foot is raised when climbing stairs."

If stairs are designed according to this principal, how should the "tread length" (see diagram) depend upon the height of each "riser"?

4 The Film Show

When a square colour slide is projected onto a screen, the area of the picture depends upon the distance of the projector from the screen as illustrated below. (When the screen is 1 metre from the projector, the picture is 20 cm × 20 cm). How does the *area* of the picture vary as the screen is moved away from the projector?

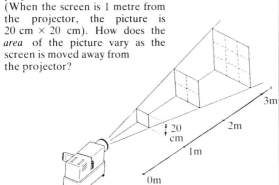

2

Regular Polygons

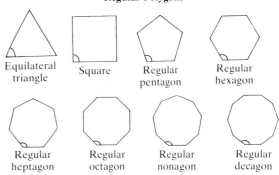

Equilateral triangle | Square | Regular pentagon | Regular hexagon

Regular heptagon | Regular octagon | Regular nonagon | Regular decagon

How does the size of one of the interior angles depend upon the number of sides of the polygon?

* Describe your answer in words and by means of a rough sketch graph.

* Draw up a table of values, and check your sketch.

(If you find this difficult, it may help if you first calculate the total sum of *all* the angles inside each polygon by subdividing it into triangles, for example:

sum of angles
= 4 × 180°
= 720°
so each angle is . . .)

* Explain, in words, how you would calculate the size of an interior angle for a regular *n* sided polygon. Can you write this as a formula?

4

The Twelve Days of Christmas

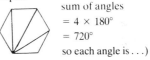

"On the first day of Christmas my true love sent to me:
A partridge in a pear tree.
On the second day of Christmas my true love sent to me:
Two turtle doves and a partridge in a pear tree.
On the third . . .

On the *twelfth* day of Christmas my true love sent to me:
12 drummers drumming, 11 pipers piping, 10 lords a-leaping, 9 ladies dancing, 8 maids a-milking, 7 swans a-swimming, 6 geese a-laying, 5 gold rings, 4 calling birds, 3 french hens, 2 turtle doves, and a partridge in a pear tree."

After twelve days, the lady counts up all her gifts.

* How many turtle doves did she receive *altogether*? (No, not two).

* If we call 'a partridge in a pear tree' the first kind of gift, a 'turtle dove' the second kind of gift . . . etc, then how many gifts of the *n* th kind were received during the twelve days? Draw up a table to show your results.

* Sketch a rough graph to illustrate your data. (You do *not* need to do this accurately).

* Which gift did she receive the most of?

* Try to find a formula to fit your data.

3

131

SOME SOLUTIONS

1. **Renting a television**

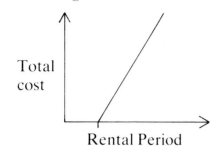

$t = 10r - 10$,
where £t = the total cost of renting the set,
and r months = the rental period.
(A step function would be a better model).

2. **The depreciating car**

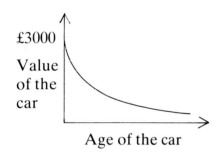

$v = 3000 \times (0.8)^a$
where £v = the value of the car
and a years = the age of the car.

3. **Staircases**

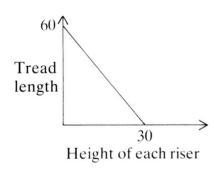

$t = 60 - 2h$
where t cm = the tread length
and h cm = the height of each riser.

4. **The film show**

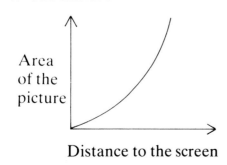

$a = 400d^2$
where a cm² = the area of the picture
and d m = the distance from the projector
to the screen.

The Twelve Days of Christmas

Altogether, the lady received 22 turtle doves (2 turtle doves on 11 occasions).
Altogether, over the twelve days,

	Total
1 Partridge was received on 12 occasions	$1 \times 12 = 12$
2 Turtle doves were received on 11 occasions	$2 \times 11 = 22$
3 French hens were received on 10 occasions	$3 \times 10 = 30$
. . . .	
12 Drummers were received on 1 occasion	$12 \times 1 = 12$

This results in the following table:

nth gift	1	2	3	4	5	6	7	8	9	10	11	12
total number received	12	22	30	36	40	42	42	40	36	30	22	12

The graph which results is shown below:

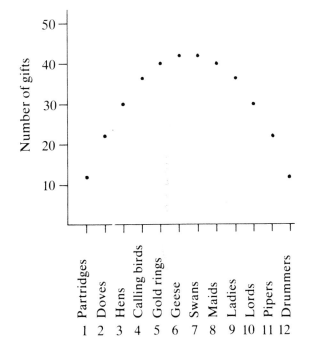

More swans and geese were received than any other gift.

A formula which fits this graph is
$$y = x(13 - x)$$
where $y =$ number of gifts received

and $x =$ the numerical label given to each gift.

(The points on this graph should, strictly, not be joined up, as intermediate values have no meaning. However, since we only asked the pupils to sketch a rough graph, they may well have illustrated the data with a continuous line.)

Regular Polygons

The graph and table drawn below illustrate how the interior angle of a regular polygon depends upon the number of sides of the polygon.

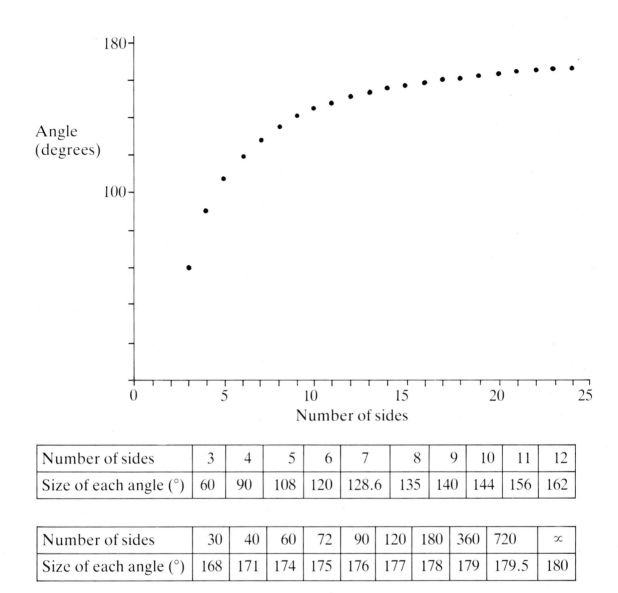

Number of sides	3	4	5	6	7	8	9	10	11	12
Size of each angle (°)	60	90	108	120	128.6	135	140	144	156	162

Number of sides	30	40	60	72	90	120	180	360	720	∞
Size of each angle (°)	168	171	174	175	176	177	178	179	179.5	180

The formula corresponding to this data is:

$a = 180 - \dfrac{360}{n}$ where a degrees = the size of each angle.

n = the number of sides.

Again, strictly speaking, we cannot join the points on the graph with a continuous line as 'there is no such thing as a regular polygon with 2½ sides, or π sides etc'...or is there?

In a fascinating article‡, David Fielker explains how an unexpected investigation resulted when this question was taken seriously:

"For the sake of completeness they discussed a polygon with two sides. It should have an angle of 0°. They produced a formula in the form

$$n \rightarrow 180 - \frac{360}{n}$$

and this verified their intuition. It also seemed reasonable that as n became larger and larger, the angle became closer and closer to 180°.

It was a nice-looking graph. They could 'see' the curve. Should they draw it in?

Well, no. Not unless the rational points in between meant something. Could we, for instance, have a regular polygon with 2½ sides?

It is in the nature of mathematics that questions like this can be taken seriously. This is one of the things that distinguishes mathematics from, say, physics. And although geometry seems to depend so much on intuition and imagery, one need not falter when intuition breaks down, but can continue in a more analytic way.

After all, we could see where the point was on the graph: 2½ sides should have an angle of around 40°. Calculation indeed showed that it was 36°.

(Note that I am now talking about 'we' rather than 'they'. At this stage I too am exploring new territory.)

Undeterred by intuition, we decided to construct this polygon, using the only usable information, that it was regular, i.e. all the sides were equal and each angle was 36°.

The result appears overleaf, so the reader can choose which way to be surprised!

‡ This extract is reprinted from "Removing the Shackles of Euclid" by David Fielker, one of a series of books entitled 'Readings in Mathematical Education' published by the Association of Teachers of Mathematics, Kings Chambers, Queen Street, Derby DE1 3DA.

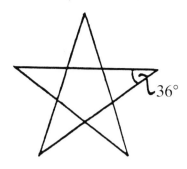

It needed a few more examples, and some rationalisation (no pun intended!) rather than a complete explanation. It made more sense if our 2½ was written as 5/2, and we could now establish an interpretation for the numerator and the denominator. We looked at a 7/2,

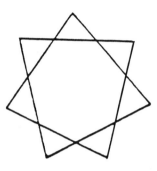

and a 7/3,

and saw that a 7/4 looked the same as a 7/3. We could have an 8/3,

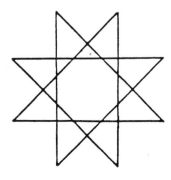

and even an 8/2,

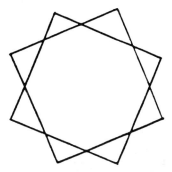

but we noted that an 8/2 was not the same as a 4/1, which was a square, although the angle was the same! Evidently each point on the graph represented a set of (star) polygons each having the same angle.

So, could we now go back to the graph and join up the points, since we now had a meaning for all the rational points?

Yes, they said.

No, said John. Because that would also include all the *irrational* points, and we had not yet found a meaning for those.

And we did not, because even *I* thought we had got sufficient out of the exercise, and it was time to move on to other things three months before the examination! Nor did we extend the graph backwards and try to interpret negative angles (e.g., a polygon with 1½ sides having an angle of −90°). But someone should."

FINDING FUNCTIONS IN TABLES OF DATA

Try the following problem. When you have finished, or when you get stuck, *read on*.

Dropping a stone

That's funny—when Galileo did it, it worked perfectly

Time (seconds)	0	1	2	3	4	5
Distance fallen (metres)	0	5	20	45	80	125

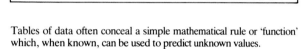

* Sketch a rough graph to illustrate this data.

* Can you see any rules or patterns in this table? Describe them in words and, if possible, by formulae.

* A stone is dropped from an aircraft. How far will it fall in 10 seconds?

Tables of data often conceal a simple mathematical rule or 'function' which, when known, can be used to predict unknown values.

This function can be very difficult to find, especially if the table contains rounded numbers or experimental errors.

It helps a great deal if you can recognise a function from the shape of its graph. On the next page is a 'rogue's gallery' of some of the most important functions.

* Which graph looks most like your sketch for the 'dropping a stone' problem?

1

1. Speed conversion chart

Miles per hour	10	20	30	40	50	60	70	80
Kilometres per hour	16.1	32.2	48.3	64.4		96.6	112.7	128.7

2. Radio frequencies and wavelengths

			Radio 4					
Frequency (KHz)	100	200	300	400	500	600	700	800
Wavelength (m)	3000	1500	1000	750	600	500	429	375

		Radio 2		Radio 1			Radio 3
Frequency (KHz)	900	909	1000	1089	1100	1200	1215
Wavelength (m)	333		300		273	250	

3. A Pendulum Clock

Length of pendulum (cm)	Time for 100 swings (seconds)
0	0
5	45
10	63
15	77
20	89
25	100
30	110
35	118
40	126
45	134
50	141
60	

4. Temperature conversion

Celsius	Fahrenheit
100	212
95	203
90	194
85	185
80	176
75	167
70	158
65	149
60	140
55	131
50	
45	113
40	104
35	95
30	86
25	77
20	68
15	59
10	50
5	41
0	32
−5	23
−10	14
−15	5
−17.8	0
−50	

4

"Rogue's Gallery"

Linear

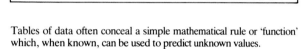

$y = Ax$ $y = Ax + B$ $y = Ax - B$ $y = -Ax + B$

Quadratic

$y = Ax^2$ $y = Ax^2 + B$ $y = -Ax^2 + B$ $y = A\sqrt{x}$

Reciprocal

$y = \dfrac{A}{x}$ $y = \dfrac{A}{x} + B$ $y = -\dfrac{A}{x} + B$

A and B are numbers greater than 0

Exponential

$y = AB^x \ (B > 1)$ $y = AB^x \ (B < 1)$

Extend this collection whenever you meet a new function . . .

2

Fitting a formula to the data

By now, you have probably realised that the graph labelled $y = Ax^2$ is the only one which fits the 'dropping a stone' data.

In our case

y = distance fallen (metres)

x = time (seconds)

and A is fixed positive number.

* Try to find the value of A that makes the function fit the data either by trial and error or by substituting for values of x and y and solving the resulting equation.

* Use your resulting formula to find out how far the stone will fall in ten seconds.

Now look at the tables on the next page
* Sketch a *rough* graph to illustrate the type of function shown in each table. (You do *not* need to plot points accurately).
* Try to find patterns or rules in the tables and write about them.
* Use the "Rogue's gallery" to try to fit a function to the data in each table.
* Some of the entries in the tables have been hidden by ink blots. Try to find out what these entries should be.

3

138

SOME SOLUTIONS

Dropping a stone

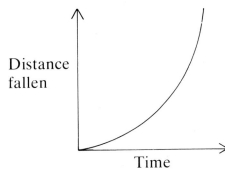

$d = 5t^2$
where d metres is the distance fallen
in t seconds. After 10 seconds, the stone will fall
500 metres.

Speed conversion chart

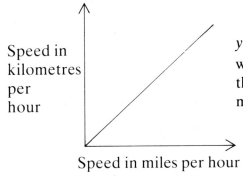

$y = 1.61x$
where x is the speed in miles per hour and y is
the speed in kilometres per hour. A speed of 50
mph corresponds to a speed of 80.5 kph.

Radio frequencies and wavelengths

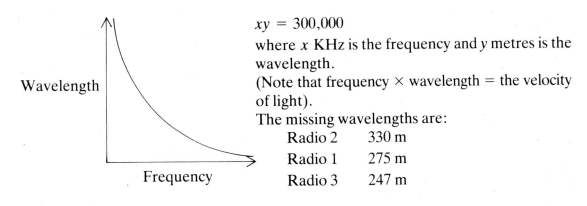

$xy = 300,000$
where x KHz is the frequency and y metres is the
wavelength.
(Note that frequency × wavelength = the velocity
of light).
The missing wavelengths are:

Radio 2	330 m
Radio 1	275 m
Radio 3	247 m

A Pendulum Clock

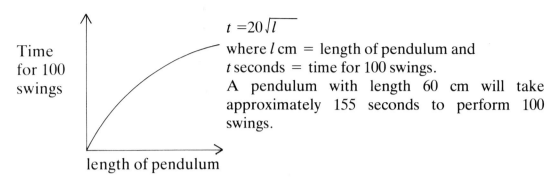

$t = 20\sqrt{l}$

where l cm = length of pendulum and
t seconds = time for 100 swings.
A pendulum with length 60 cm will take
approximately 155 seconds to perform 100
swings.

Temperature conversion

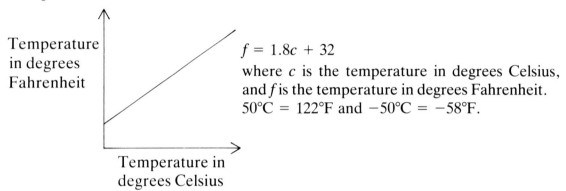

$f = 1.8c + 32$

where c is the temperature in degrees Celsius,
and f is the temperature in degrees Fahrenheit.
50°C = 122°F and −50°C = −58°F.

A Problem Collection

CONTENTS

INTRODUCTION

This collection is intended to supplement the classroom materials presented in Units A and B. It is divided into two sections, "Problems" and "Graphs and other data for interpretation".

The first section contains 9 problems which can all be solved graphically. All but one of the problems is accompanied by a separate selection of hints which may be supplied to pupils who need more detailed guidance. These problems are challenging and pupils should expect to have to struggle with each one for some time before success is achieved. It is not intended that pupils should have to attempt every problem but that two or three should be selected and pursued in some depth. Below, we give some guidance on how this selection may be made.

The second section presents a collection of shorter situations which are intended to provide more straightforward practice at interpreting data, and these items therefore tend to be easier than the problem solving situations presented in the first part. This section should not be treated as a collection which has to be worked through in a concentrated, ordered way but rather as a selection of ideas which can be dipped into and used from time to time as is felt appropriate. Solutions have not peen provided for this section.

PROBLEMS

Suggested Presentation

As these problems are fairly demanding, it is helpful if pairs or small groups of pupils are allowed to work *cooperatively* in an *unhurried* atmosphere. Pupils are much more likely to achieve success if they are given problems which are pitched at a suitable level of difficulty and which concern a situation of some interest. It is therefore desirable to offer each group a selection of problems from which they can choose just a few (e.g., three) to work on over a given period (e.g., a week). The table shown overleaf should help you to select suitable problems, but it is advisable to read through each problem carefully before coming to a final decision.

You will notice that each situation (except the last) begins with a *problem statement* and this is followed by a *list of hints* which offer more detailed step-by-step guidance. ("The Missing Planet" is a longer, more involved situation and we have therefore decided that the problem-hint format is unsuitable.) We suggest that, initially, you only issue the problem statements. This will encourage pupils to explore and discuss *their own ideas* for solving the problems. If they run out of ideas or become completely bogged down, then the hints may be supplied either on paper or orally.

Full answers have been supplied to the problems, but these should not be regarded as definitive. (Many problems can be solved without using graphs or algebra.) Pupils should not be discouraged from pursuing a solution that appears very different from those supplied.

Summary of problem situations

Designing a water tank

To maximise the volume of a tank which can be constructed from a square sheet of metal. This involves maximising the cubic function $v = 4x(1 - x)^2$ (where $0 < x < 1$), graphically.

The point of no return

To find the time and distance a pilot can fly before he has to turn back for home, assuming that he only has a limited quantity of fuel and a steady wind is blowing. To generalise these results for different wind speeds. This involves drawing pairs of linear graphs (using knowledge about their gradients) and finding their points of intersection.

Warmsnug double glazing

To discover a pattern in unsorted data and use it to spot an error and discover a rule behind the data. A scattergraph approach is useful. The function involved has two variables, and takes the form $p = a + 2l$, where £p is the price of a window which uses l feet of wood for the frame, and contains a square feet of glass.

Producing a magazine

To consider the important decisions that must be made when producing a home made magazine and to decide on a selling price in order to maximise the profit made. This involves constructing and maximising two quadratic functions
$p = (100 - 2s)s$ and $p = (100 - 2s)(s - 10)$

The Ffestiniog railway

To design a workable railway timetable fulfilling a list of practical constraints. This is best done by fitting several linear distance-time graphs together and reading off arrival times at various stations.

Carbon dating

To discover the meaning of the term "half life", and how an archaeological find may be dated. This involves solving an exponential equation $a = 15.3 \times 0.886^t$ where various values of a are given. As no knowledge of logarithms is assumed, this can be done graphically.

Designing a can

To minimise the surface area (α cost) of metal used when a cylindrical can with a given volume is to be manufactured. This involves minimising the function
$s = \dfrac{1000}{r} + 2\pi r^2$, graphically.

Manufacturing a computer

To optimise the profit made by a small business which assembles and sells two types of computer. This is a challenging linear programming problem.

The missing plant

A more extended situation requiring a variety of problem solving skills. Pattern recognition (using scattergraphs) and formula fitting both play an important part in forming hypotheses about the characteristics of a planet which, perhaps, used to lie between Mars and Jupiter millions of years ago.

DESIGNING A WATER TANK

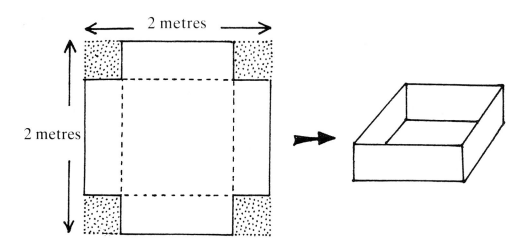

A square metal sheet (2 metres by 2 metres) is to be made into an open-topped water tank by cutting squares from the four corners of the sheet, and bending the four remaining rectangular pieces up, to form the sides of the tank. These edges will then be welded together.

* How will the final volume of the tank depend upon the size of the squares cut from the corners?

  Describe your answer by:

  a) Sketching a rough graph

  b) explaining the shape of your graph in words

  c) trying to find an algebraic formula

* How large should the four corners be cut, so that the resulting volume of the tank is as large as possible?

146

DESIGNING A WATER TANK ... SOME HINTS

*   Imagine cutting very small squares from the corners of the metal sheet. In your mind, fold the sheet up. Will the resulting volume be large or small? Why?

Now imagine cutting out larger and larger squares . . . .

What are the largest squares you can cut? What will the resulting volume be?

*   Sketch a rough graph to describe your thoughts and explain it fully in words underneath:

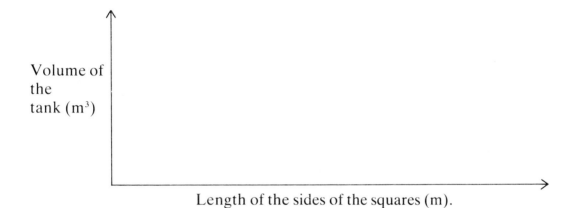

*   In order to find a formula, imagine cutting a square x metres by x metres from each corner of the sheet. Find an expression for the resulting volume.

*   Now try plotting an accurate graph.
(A suitable scale is 1 cm represents 0.1 metres on the horizontal axis, and 1 cm represents 0.1 cubic metres on the vertical axis).

How good was your sketch?

*   *Use your graph* to find out how large the four corner squares should be cut, so that the resulting volume is maximised.

147

SOLUTIONS TO "DESIGNING A WATER TANK"

This problem is considerably enhanced if a practical approach is adopted. A supply of scissors and 20 cm by 20 cm cardboard squares will enable pupils to construct scale models (1:10) of a number of different water tanks. (Calculators will be needed to help with the evaluation of the volumes). Challenge each group of pupils to make the "largest" water tank (i.e., the one with the greatest capacity) from the given square of cardboard.

Initially, few pupils are likely to adopt an algebraic approach. Usually, pupils prefer to begin by conducting a series of random experiments until they have acquired a strong intuitive 'feel' for the situation, and only then consider adopting a more systematic method. This, a most natural sequence of events, should not be discouraged or hurried.

Below, we give a graphical solution to the problem:

The relationship between the volume of the box (v cubic metres) and the size of the square (x metres by x metres) cut from each corner is given by

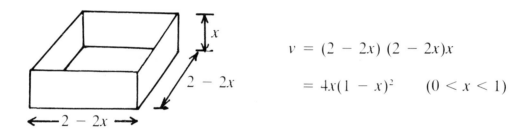

$$v = (2 - 2x)(2 - 2x)x$$

$$= 4x(1 - x)^2 \qquad (0 < x < 1)$$

A suitable table of values is given below:

x	0	0.1	0.2	0.3	0.4	0.5	0.6	0.7	0.8	0.9	1
v	0	0.324	0.512	0.588	0.576	0.5	0.384	0.252	0.128	0.036	0

The table results in the following graph:

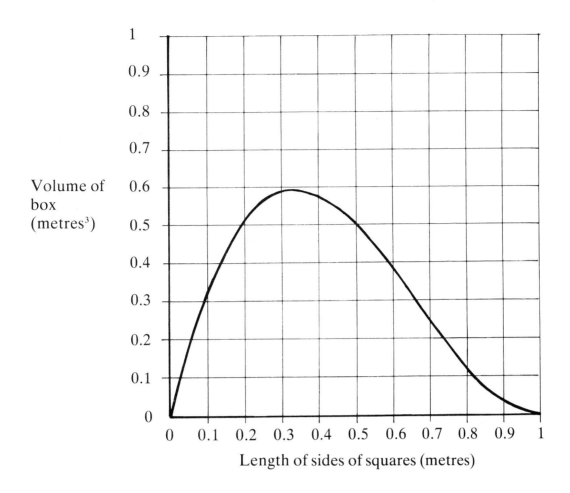

The maximum volume of 0.593m³ occurs when $x = 0.33$ metres

THE POINT OF NO RETURN

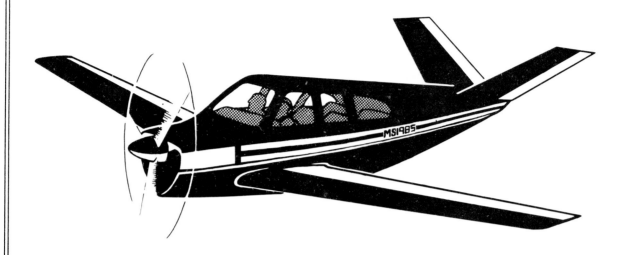

Imagine that you are the pilot of the light aircraft in the picture, which is capable of cruising at a steady speed of 300 km/h in still air. You have enough fuel on board to last four hours.

You take off from the airfield and, on the outward journey, are helped along by a 50 km/h wind which increases your cruising speed relative to the ground to 350 km/h.

Suddenly you realise that on your return journey you will be flying *into* the wind and will therefore slow down to 250 km/h.

* What is the maximum distance that you can travel from the airfield, and still be sure that you have enough fuel left to make a safe return journey?

* Investigate these 'points of no return' for different wind speeds.

THE POINT OF NO RETURN . . . SOME HINTS

* Draw a graph to show how your distance from the airfield will vary with time.
How can you show an outward speed of 350 km/h?
How can you show a return speed of 250 km/h?

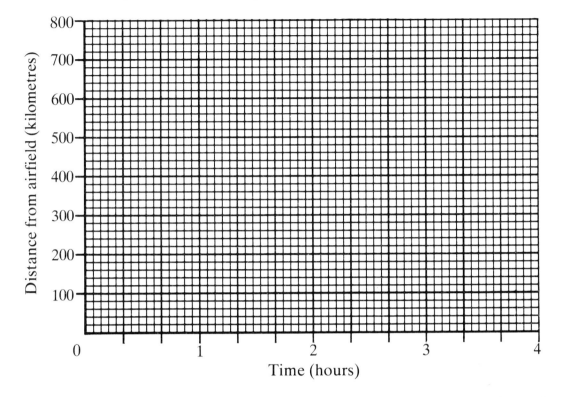

* Use your graph to find the maximum distance you can travel from the airfield, and the time at which you should turn round.

* On the same graph, investigate the 'points of no return' for different wind speeds. What kind of pattern do these points make on the graph paper?
Can you explain why?

* Suppose the windspeed is w km/h,
the 'point of no return' is d km from the airfield
and the time at which you should turn round is t hours.

Write down two expressions for the outward speed of the aircraft, one involving w and one involving d and t.

Write down two expressions for the homeward speed of the aircraft, one involving w and one involving d and t.

Try to express d in terms of only t, by eliminating w from the two resulting equations.

Does this explain the pattern made by your 'points of no return'?

SOLUTIONS TO "THE POINT OF NO RETURN"

A graphical approach to this problem is probably the most accessible. With a 50 km/h wind, the point of no return can be found by finding the intersection of two straight lines, one through the origin with a gradient of 350 (km/h) and the other through the point (4,0) with a gradient of −250 (km/h).

The maximum distance that can be travelled is about 580 kilometres (or, more precisely, 583 kilometres) and the pilot must turn round after 1 hour 40 minutes.

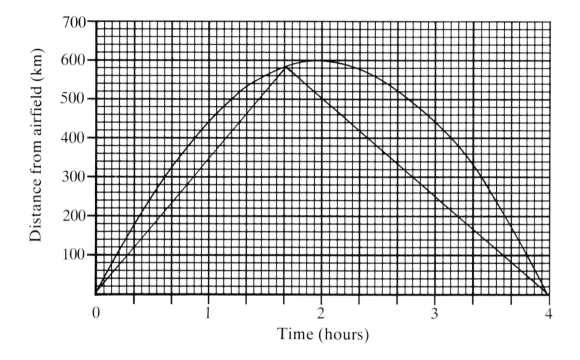

When several 'points of no return' are found for different wind speeds, it may be seen that they lie in the parabola

$$d = 150t(4 - t)$$

where d kilometres = maximum distance travelled from airfield
and t hours = time at which the aircraft must turn for home.

This is illustrated on the front cover of this Module book.

This formula is derived below:

Suppose the windspeed is w km/h.

The outward speed of the aircraft $= 300 + w = \dfrac{d}{t}$ (km/h) —①

The homeward speed of the aircraft $= 300 - w = \dfrac{d}{4 - t}$ (km/h) —②

Adding ① and ② we obtain

$$600 = \frac{d}{t} + \frac{d}{(4 - t)} \Rightarrow d = 150t(4 - t)$$

Other results which may be obtained are:

$$t = 2 - \frac{w}{150}$$

$$d = \frac{1}{150}\,(300 + w)\,(300 - w)$$

These formulae can be used to determine the time at which the aircraft must turn and the range of the aircraft for any given windspeed.

"WARMSNUG DOUBLE GLAZING"

(The windows on this sheet are all drawn to scale: 1 cm represents 1 foot).

* How have "Warmsnug" arrived at the prices shown on these windows?

* Which window has been given an incorrect price? How much should it cost?

* Explain your reasoning clearly.

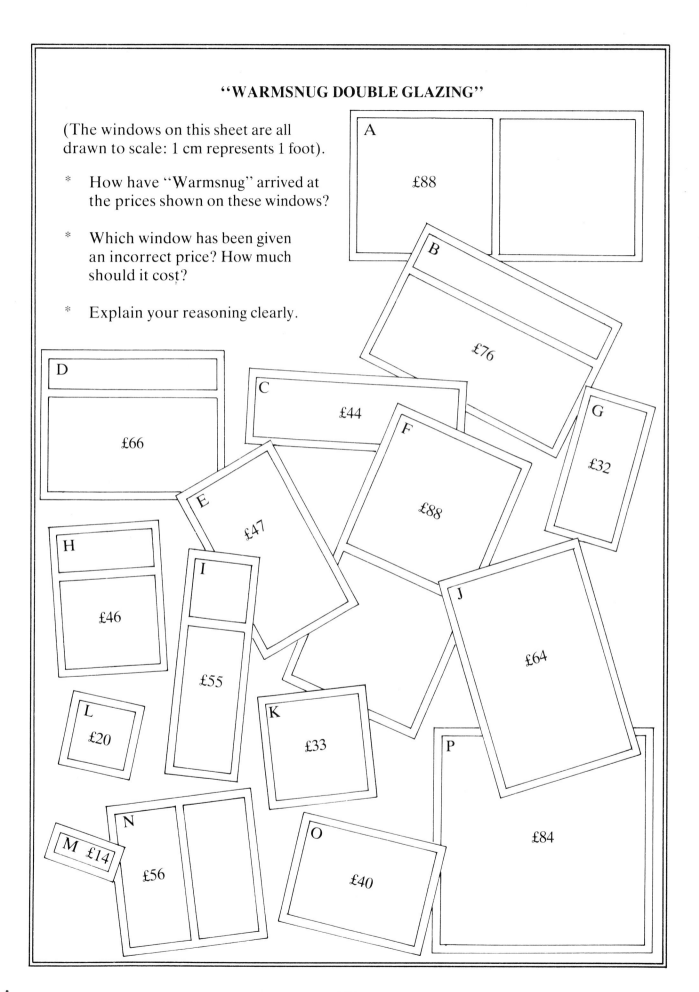

A £88

B £76

C £44

D £66

E £47

F £88

G £32

H £46

I £55

J £64

K £33

L £20

M £14

N £56

O £40

P £84

"WARMSNUG" DOUBLE GLAZING ... SOME HINTS

* Write down a list of factors which *may* affect the price that "Warmsnug" ask for any particular window:

  e.g.   Perimeter,
         Area of glass needed,
         . . . .
         . . . .

* Using your list, examine the pictures of the windows in a systematic manner.

* Draw up a table, showing all the data which you think may be relevant. (Can you share this work out among other members of your group?)

* Which factors or combinations of factors is the most important in determining the price?

  Draw scattergraphs to test your ideas. For example, if you think that the perimeter is the most important factor, you could draw a graph showing:

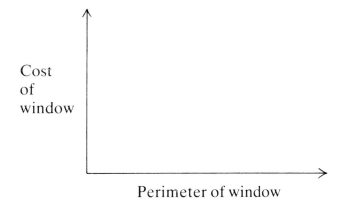

* Does your graph confirm your ideas? If not, you may have to look at some other factors.

* Try to find a point which does not follow the general trend on your graph. Has this window been incorrectly priced?

* Try to find a formula which fits your graph, and which can be used to predict the price of *any* window from its dimensions.

SOLUTIONS TO "WARMSNUG" DOUBLE GLAZING

In this activity, pupils are invited to search through a collection of unsorted data in an attempt to discover some underlying rule or pattern which may then be used to spot errors and predict new results. The initial data collection may prove quite time consuming, but if a group of pupils work cooperatively, and share tasks out among group members, much time and effort may be saved. (Pupils often find it hard to work collaboratively where each member presents a different contribution to the final product. It is more common to find *every* member of a group working through *every* task.)

The table shown below summarises the information that may be extracted from the worksheet.

Window	Breadth (feet)	Height (feet)	Area of glass (feet²)	Perimeter (feet)	Length of wooden surround (feet)	Price (£)
A	8	4	32	24	28	88
B	6	4	24	20	26	76
C	6	2	12	16	16	44
D	5	4	20	18	23	66
E	3	5	15	16	16	47
F	4	8	32	24	28	88
G	2	4	8	12	12	32
H	3	4	12	14	17	46
I	2	6	12	16	18	55
J	4	6	24	20	20	64
K	3	3	9	12	12	33
L	2	2	4	8	8	20
M	2	1	2	6	6	14
N	4	4	16	16	20	56
O	4	3	12	14	14	40
P	6	6	36	24	24	84

Scattergraphs may be used to test the strength of the relationships between these factors and the overall prices. Indeed, the area of glass used and the length of the wooden surround both give strong correlations from which it is possible to identify window I as probably the one which has been incorrectly priced.

156

It seems logical to pay for the length of wood and the area of glass.

If we therefore try to fit the model

$$\text{Price} = k_1 \times \text{area} + k_2 \times \text{length of wood used,}$$

then by substitution we find that $k_1 = 1$ and $k_2 = 2$, in appropriate units. Thus the glass costs £1 per square foot, and the wooden surround costs £2 per foot.

Window I has therefore been given an incorrect price, it should be £48, not £55.

PRODUCING A MAGAZINE

A group of bored, penniless teenagers want to make some money by producing and selling their own home-made magazine. A sympathetic teacher offers to supply duplicating facilities and paper free of charge, at least for the first few issues.

1 a) Make a list of all the important decisions they must make.
      Here are three to start you off:

> How long should the magazine be?   (l pages)
>
> How many writers will be needed?   (w writers)
>
> How long will it take to write?   (t hours)

   b) Many items in your list will depend on other items.
      For example,
         For a fixed number of people involved,
         the longer the magazine, the longer
         it will take to write.

      For a fixed length of magazine,
         the more writers there are, ...

      Complete the statement, and sketch a graph
      to illustrate it.

      Write down other relationships you can find,
      and sketch graphs in each case.

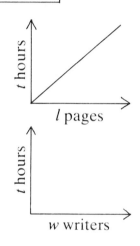

2 The group eventually decides to find out how many potential customers there are within the school, by producing a sample magazine and conducting a survey of 100 pupils, asking them "Up to how much would you be prepared to pay for this magazine?" Their data is shown below:

Selling price (s pence)	Nothing	10	20	30	40
Number prepared to pay this price (n people)	100	82	58	40	18

How much should they sell the magazine for in order to maximise their profit?

3 After a few issues, the teacher decides that he will have to charge the pupils 10p per magazine for paper and duplicating.

How much should they sell the magazine for now?

PRODUCING A MAGAZINE... SOME HINTS

1 Here is a more complete list of the important factors that must be taken into account:

Who is the magazine for?	(schoolfriends?)
What should it be about?	(news, sport, puzzles, jokes..?)
How long should it be?	(l pages)
How many writers will it need?	(w writers)
How long will it take to write?	(t hours)
How many people will buy it?	(n people)
What should we fix the selling price at?	(s pence)
How much profit will we make altogether?	(p pence)
How much should we spend on advertising?	(a pence)

* Can you think of any important factors that are *still* missing?

* Sketch graphs to show how: t depends on w; w depends on l; n depends on s; p depends on s; n depends on a.

* Explain the shape of each of your graphs in words.

2 * Draw a graph of the information given in the table of data.

* Explain the shape of the graph.

* What kind of relationship is this?
  (Can you find an approximate formula which relates n to s?)

* From this data, draw up a table of values and a graph to show how the *profit* (p pence) depends on the selling price (s pence).
  (Can you find a formula which relates p and s?)

* Use your graph to find the selling price which maximises the profit made.

3 Each magazine costs 10p to produce.
  * Suppose we fix the selling price at 20p.

  How many people will buy the magazine? How much money will be raised by selling the magazine, (the 'revenue')? How much will these magazines cost to produce? How much actual profit will therefore be made?

  * Draw up a table of data which shows how the revenue, production costs and profit all vary with the selling price of the magazine.

  * Draw a graph from your table and use it to decide on the best selling price for the magazine.

SOLUTIONS TO "PRODUCING A MAGAZINE"

This situation begins with a fairly open ended graph sketching activity, which should help pupils to become involved in the situation, and moves on to consider two specific economic problems—how can profit be maximised without and then with production costs.

1.   Some possible relationships which can be described are illustrated below:

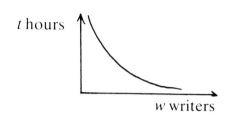

"The more writers there are, the less time it will take."

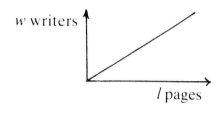

"The longer the magazine, the more writers needed."

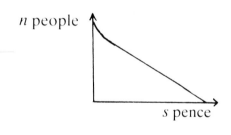

"The more you charge, the fewer that will buy."

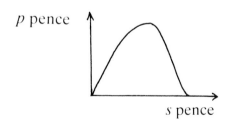

"No profit will be made on a free magazine, or on a magazine which is too expensive for anyone to buy. In between these extremes lies the optimum".

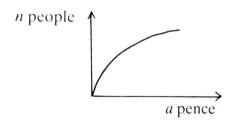

"A small amount of advertising may affect the sales considerably, but larger amounts will have a relatively diminishing effect due to "saturation".

There are, of course, other possibilities.

2. When pupils plot a graph to illustrate how the 'number of people prepared to buy the magazine' (*n* people) varies with selling price (*s* pence), they should obtain a graph which approximates to the straight line $n = 100 - 2s$.

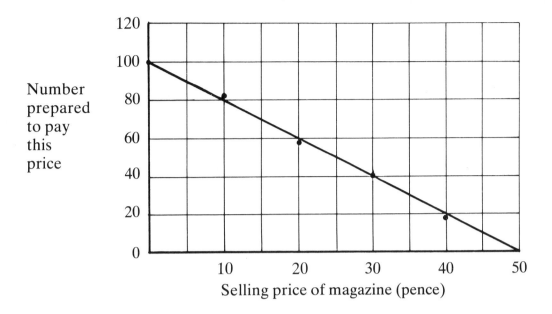

The profit made for various selling prices can be found by multiplying values of *n* by corresponding values of *s*:

Selling price (*s* pence)	Nothing	10	20	30	40
Number prepared to pay this price (*n* people)	100	82	58	40	18
Profit made (*p* pence)		0	820	1160	1200	720

This will lead to the graph shown below, from which the optimum selling price, 25 pence, and the corresponding profit, £12.50, can be read off.

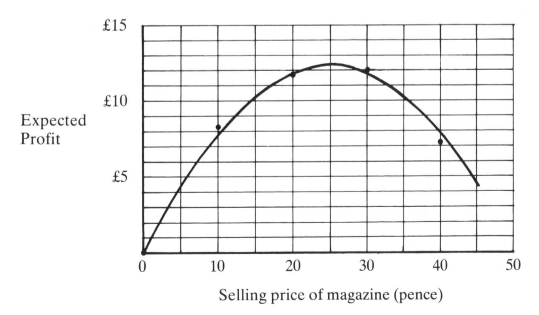

161

(Algebraically, the profit made (p pence) is approximately given by
$$p = ns = (100 - 2s)s.$$
This can be differentiated to find the optimum selling price).

3. The final problem involves taking account of production costs. The table drawn above can now be adapted to give:

Selling price (s pence)	Nothing	10	20	30	40
Number prepared to pay this price (n people)	100	82	58	40	18
Revenue (r pence)	0	820	1160	1200	720
Production costs (c pence)	1000	820	580	400	180
Profit (($p = r - c$) pence)	−1000	0	580	800	540

Algebraically we now have:

$n = 100 - 2s$ (as before)

$r = ns$ (the revenue is obtained by multiplying the price of each magazine by the number sold at that price).

$c = 10n$ (each magazine costs 10p to produce, so the production costs for n magazines is $10n$).

$p = r - c$ (the profit made = revenue − production costs).

These can be combined to give

$$p = ns - 10n = n(s - 10) = (100 - 2s)(s - 10)$$

Which results in the graph shown opposite.

From this graph, it would appear that the selling price of each magazine should now be 30 pence, resulting in an expected profit of £8.00.

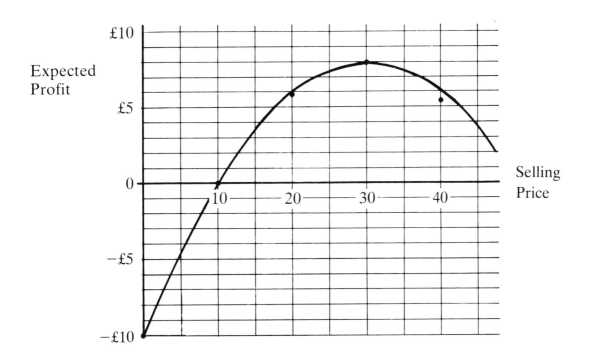

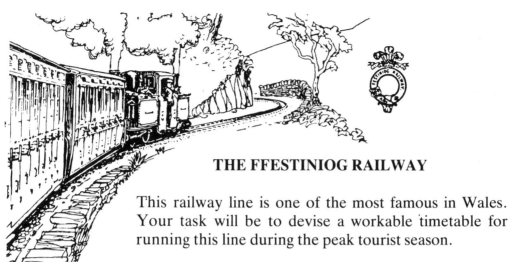

THE FFESTINIOG RAILWAY

This railway line is one of the most famous in Wales. Your task will be to devise a workable timetable for running this line during the peak tourist season.

The following facts will need to be taken into account:—

* There are 6 main stations along the 13½ mile track:

  (The distances between them are shown in miles)

* Three steam trains are to operate a shuttle service. This means that they will travel back and forth along the line from Porthmadog to Blaenau Ffestiniog with a 10-minute stop at each end. (This should provide enough time for drivers to change etc.)

* The three trains must start and finish each day at Porthmadog.

* The line is single-track. This means that trains cannot pass each other, except at specially designed passing places. (You will need to say where these will be needed. You should try to use as few passing places as possible.)

* Trains should depart from stations at regular intervals if possible.

* The journey from Porthmadog to Blaenau Ffestiniog is 65 minutes (including stops at intermediate stations. These stops are very short and may be neglected in the timetabling).

* The first train of the day will leave Porthmadog at 9.00 a.m.

* The last train must return to Porthmadog by 5.00 p.m. (These times are more restricted than those that do, in fact, operate.)

THE "FFESTINIOG RAILWAY" ... SOME HINTS

Use a copy of the graph paper provided to draw a distance-time graph for the 9.00 a.m. train leaving Porthmadog.

Try to show, accurately:

- The outward journey from Porthmadog to Blaenau Ffestiniog.
- The waiting time at Blaenau Ffestiniog.
- The return journey from Blaenau Ffestiniog to Porthmadog.
- The waiting time at Porthmadog ... and so on.

What is the interval between departure times from Porthmadog for the above train?

How can we space the two other trains regularly between these departure times?

Draw similar graphs for the other two trains.

How many passing places are needed? Where will these have to be?

From your graph, complete the following timetable:

Miles	Station		Daily Timetable					
0	Porthmadog	d	09.00					
2	Minffordd	d						
3¼	Penrhyn	d						
7½	Tan-y-Bwlch	d						
12¼	Tanygrisiau	d						
13½	Blaenau Ffestiniog	a						
0	Blaenau Ffestiniog	d						
1¼	Tanygrisiau	d						
6	Tan-y-Bwlch	d						
10¼	Penrhyn	d						
11½	Minffordd	d						
13½	Porthmadog	a						

Ask your teacher for a copy of the real timetable, and write about how it compares with your own.

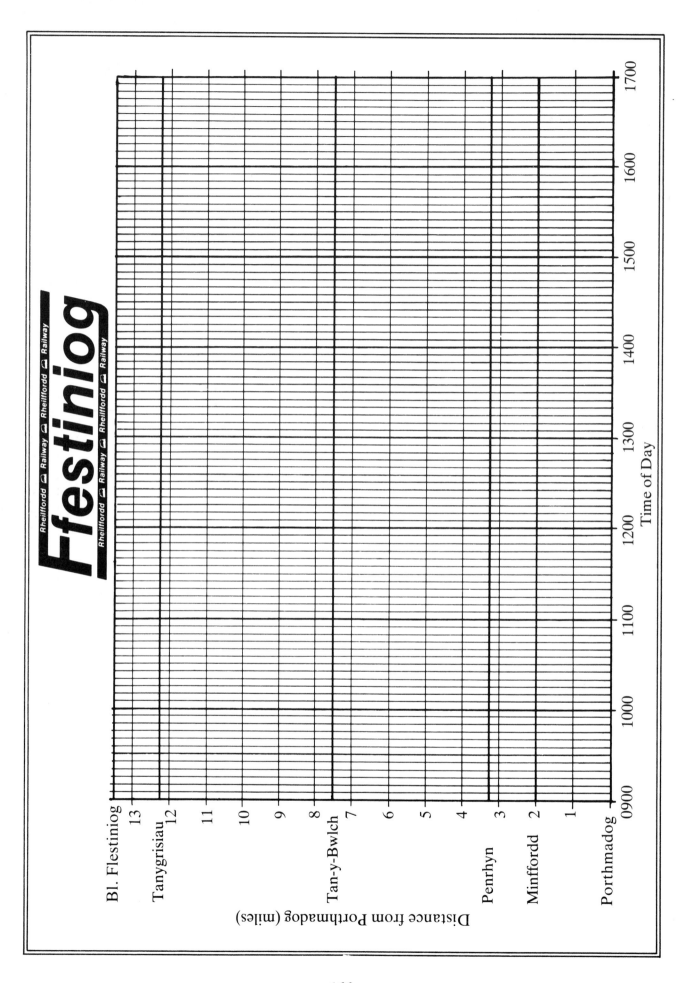

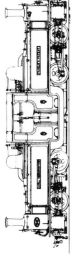

Ffestiniog

Rheilffordd ⚙ Railway ⚙ Rheilffordd ⚙ Railway ⚙ Rheilffordd ⚙ Railway

Porthmadog to Blaenau Ffestiniog

Time Table 1985

CHILDREN FREE

one passenger (under 16) travels free for each adult paying normal 3rd class fare

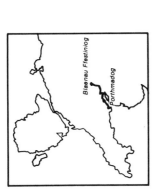

MORE MILES FOR YOUR MONEY

THIRD CLASS (First class available at supplementary charge)

Principal Fares (available in either direction)	ORDINARY SINGLE	ORDINARY RETURN	ECONOMY RETURN ★
Porthmadog to Blaenau Ffestiniog	£2.80	£5.60	£4.60
Porthmadog to Tan-y-Bwlch	£1.70	£3.40	—
Tan-y-Bwlch to Blaenau Ffestiniog	£1.70	£3.40	—
Porthmadog to Penrhyn	90p	£1.80	—

★ Travel out by diesel service shown black on timetable. Return by ANY train.

Reductions for Children and Senior Citizens as follows:

Children under 5 free. ONE CHILD UNDER 16 TRAVELS FREE IN THIRD CLASS FOR EACH ADULT PAYING THIRD CLASS ORDINARY OR ECONOMY FARES. Additional children aged 5 and under 16 travel at half fare.

Senior Citizens travel at half fare on return fares only.

PLEASE NOTE FREE CHILD FACILITY

Family Fares up to 22% cheaper than three years ago!

Fares correct at time of going to press but liable to alteration without notice.

Did you know . . . .
that the Ffestiniog Railway has a supporters club?

The FESTINIOG RAILWAY SOCIETY

is a voluntary organisation dedicated to supporting the continued existence of the Ffestiniog Railway.

You can join at one of the Railway's shops, or, send £6 for Juniors under the age of 18) to the Membership Secretary: J. Manisty, 4 Kingsgate Street, Winchester, Hants. SO23 9PD. (Members receive travel privileges and a quarterly magazine.)

If you would like further information about the Ffestiniog Railway and the Society, ask at the booking office for a copy of the leaflet. *An introduction to the Festiniog Railway Society.*

Ffestiniog Railway, Porthmadog, Gwynedd.
Telephone No.: (0766) 2340/2384
Member — Ten Top Attractions of North Wales

Published by the Ffestiniog Railway, Porthmadog, Gwynedd, and printed by T. Stephenson & Sons Ltd, Prescot, Merseyside

---

Ffestiniog

Rheilffordd ⚙ Railway ⚙ Rheilffordd ⚙ Railway ⚙ Rheilffordd ⚙ Railway

MOUNTAINS, LAKES AND COASTLINE

Take the famous Ffestiniog Railway for a memorable journey through the Snowdonia National Park. From the coast at Porthmadog the little train climbs through tranquil pastures and magnificent forests, past lakes and waterfalls, round horseshoe bends and even a complete spiral, sometimes clinging to the side of the mountain and sometimes tunnelling under it. Much of the area is so remote that there are not even any motor roads and the train stops occasionally at isolated cottages whose inhabitants depend entirely on the railway. 13½ miles and one hour's journey time from Porthmadog is Blaenau Ffestiniog, over 700 feet above sea level. Here are the slate mines at Llechwedd and Gloddfa Ganol which are both open to visitors.

To cater for all your requirements there are gift shops at Porthmadog, Tan-y-Bwlch and Blaenau Ffestiniog, a self-service restaurant at Porthmadog and station buffets at Tan-y-Bwlch and Blaenau Ffestiniog.

So sit back, relax and take the journey of a lifetime. Let our stewards wait on you with snacks and drinks from the buffet car or minibar trolley. For the enthusiast, there's even more — many of the trains are pulled by unique and historic steam locomotives some of which have served the line for over a hundred years.

Your complete day out . . . .
SPECIAL INCLUSIVE EXCURSIONS
FROM PORTHMADOG

STWLAN DAM (Daily 26 May to 13 September)
Depart Porthmadog by most "daytime" trains (see timetable) for bus connection from Tanygrisiau. This is one of the most spectacular bus routes in Britain, ascending to a height of 1650 feet. The bus returns to Tanygrisiau station from where you may return to Porthmadog or, if you so wish, continue your rail journey to Blaenau Ffestiniog at no extra charge. Allow 2½ hours for the complete excursion if returning direct from Tanygrisiau or 3 hours 20 minutes if returning via Blaenau Ffestiniog.

LLECHWEDD CAVERNS (Monday to Saturday 30 March to 2 November, also Sundays 26 May to 8 September)
Depart Porthmadog by any train up to 1220 (1310 when operating). Transfer to 'bus at Blaenau Ffestiniog for short trip across town to Llechwedd Caverns. Then take either the battery electric train or the deep mine incline into the heart of a Victorian slate mine. Allow at least 5 hours to do justice to the complete excursion.

FFESTINIOG LINK TOURS (Monday to Friday 27 May to 13 September)
The new joint Ffestiniog/British Rail station in Blaenau Ffestiniog has enabled us to provide easy rail access to the Conwy Valley and North Wales Coast. The journey from Porthmadog to Llandudno offers 44 miles of spectacular mountain and coastal scenery. Depart Porthmadog at 0950 (or 0840 when operating) for this highlight of your holiday. A shorter version of this tour from Porthmadog to Betws-y-Coed or Llanrwst is also available.

GLODDFA GANOL Slate Mine. Free admission will be granted during the 1985 season to any child whose parent produces a full return Ffestiniog ticket between Porthmadog and Blaenau Ffestiniog. A 'bus service operates between Porthmadog and Gloddfa Ganol.

The Great Little Trains of Wales

NARROW GAUGE WANDERER TICKET

GREAT VALUE — 8 days unlimited travel on any of the following lines: FFESTINIOG RAILWAY, TALYLLYN RAILWAY, VALE OF RHEIDOL RAILWAY, BALA LAKE RAILWAY, WELSHPOOL AND LLANFAIR LIGHT RAILWAY, LLANBERIS LAKE RAILWAY, WELSH HIGHLAND RAILWAY, BRECON MOUNTAIN RAILWAY.

Adults: £13   Children aged 5 and under 16: £6.50.

HIGH SUMMER	Monday 15 July to Friday 30 August (Also Spring Holiday Week Sunday 26 May to Thursday 30 May)																		
	MONDAYS TO THURSDAYS											FRIDAYS, SATURDAYS AND SUNDAYS							
Porthmadog d.	**0840**	0950	1035	1125	1220	1310	1400	1455	1545	1635	**1900**	0950	**1035**	1125	1220	**1310**	1400	1455	163
British Rail Cambrian Coast line (See notes below) NO SUNDAY SERVICE — Pwllheli d.	0755		0938		1135			1400	1500		1640	0755g	0938		1135			1400	150
Minffordd a.	0825		1008		1205			1433	1530		1710	0825g	1008		1205			1433	153
Barmouth d.		0817		0955		1155		1343		1520	1752	0817		0955		1155FO	1247SO	1343	152
Minffordd a.		0901		1040		1237		1422		1606	1834	0901		1040		1237FO	1325SO	1422	160
Minffordd d.	**0849**	0959	1044	1134	1229	1319	1409	1504	1554	1644	**1909**	0959	**1044**	1134	1229	**1319**	1409	1504	164
Penrhyn d.	**“Early Bird”**	1005	1050	1140	1235	1325	1415	1510	1600	1650	**1915**	1005	**1050**	1140	1235	**1325**	1415	1510	165
Tan-y-Bwlch d.		1025	1112	1205	1255	1345	1435	1530	1620	1710	**1935**	1025	**1112**	1205	1255	**1345**	1435	1530	171
Tanygrisiau d.		1043	1135	1223	1313	1407	1458	1548	1641	1728	**1953**	1043	**1135**	1223	1313	**1407**	1458	1548	172
Bl. Ffestiniog a.	**0940**	1055	1146	1233	1325	1417	1507	1600	1652	1740	**2005**	1055	**1146**	1233	1325	**1417**	1507	1600	174
British Rail Conwy Valley line (See notes below) NO SUNDAY SERVICE — Bl. Ffestiniog d.	0945	1105			1330	1450		1625		1748	2020	1105FO			1330	1450		1625	174
Llandudno Jcn. a.	1042	1204			1431	1548		1726		1845	2117	1204FO			1431	1548		1726	184
Llandudno a.	1055	1214			1441	1558		1736		1903	2127	1214FO			1441	1558		1736	190
Llandudno d.	0830	0950		1110			1333	1450		1630	1745	0830 0950FO		1110			1333	1450	163
Llandudno Jcn. d.	0840	1000		1121			1343	1501		1640	1803	0840 1000FO		1121			1343	1501	164
Bl. Ffestiniog a.	0940	1100		1224			1445	1609		1741	1903	0940 1100FO		1224			1445	1609	174
Bl. Ffestiniog d.	**1015**	1105	1155	1245	1340	1430	1520	1615	1700	1746	**2015**	1105	**1155**	1245	1340	**1430**	1520	1615	174
Tanygrisiau d.	**1021**	1111	1201	1251	1346	1436	1526	1621	1706	1752	**2021**	1111	**1201**	1251	1346	**1436**	1526	1621	175
Tan-y-Bwlch d.	**1045**	1133	1225	1315	1405	1500	1550	1640	1730	1814	**2043**	1133	**1225**	1315	1405	**1500**	1550	1640	181
Penrhyn d.	**1101**	1149	1245	1335	1424	1520	1606	1659	1746	1830	**2059**	1149	**1245**	1335	1424	**1520**	1606	1659	183
Minffordd d.	**1106**	1154	1250	1340	1429	1525	1611	1706	1751	1835	**2104**	1154	**1250**	1340	1429	**1525**	1611	1706	183
British Rail Cambrian Coast line (See notes below) NO SUNDAY SERVICE — Minffordd d.		1205		1433	1530		1710			1955		1205		1433	1530		1710		1955
Barmouth a.		1246		1514	1616		1751			2036		1246		1514	1616		1751		2036
Minffordd d.		1237		1422		1606			1834		2212	1237FO	1325SO	1422		1606		1834	2212
Pwllheli a.		1305		1450		1633			1901		2239	1305FO	1353SO	1450		1633		1901	2239
Porthmadog a.	**1120**	1209	1304	1354	1444	1539	1629	1719	1805	1848	**2117**	1209	**1304**	1354	1444	**1539**	1625	1719	184

AUTUMN AND WINTER	Saturday 31 August to Sunday 15 September											DAILY Monday 16 Sept. to Sunday 3 Nov.			Daily 26 Dec to 1 Jan Sats & Suns 15 Feb 1986 to 23 March 1986	
	MONDAYS TO FRIDAYS								SATS. & SUNS.							
Porthmadog d.	0950	**1035**	1125	1220	**1310**	1400	1455	1635	0950	1220	1455	0950	1220	**1455**	**1115**	**1455**
British Rail Cambrian Coast line (See notes below) NO SUNDAY SERVICE — Pwllheli d.	0755	0938		1135				1500	0838	1135	1400	0755g	1135		0938	1135
Minffordd a.	0825	1008		1205				1530	0911	1205	1433	0825g	1205		1008	1205
Barmouth d.	0817		0955				1343	1520	0817	0955	1343	0817	0955	1343	0955	1343
Minffordd a.	0901		1040				1422	1606	0901	1040	1422	0901	1040	1422	1040	1422
Minffordd d.	0959	**1044**	1134	1229	**1319**	1409	1504	1644	0959	1229	1504	0959	1229	**1504**	**1124**	**1504**
Penrhyn d.	1005	**1050**	1140	1235	**1325**	1415	1510	1650	1005	1235	1510	1005	1235	**1510**	**1130**	**1510**
Tan-y-Bwlch d.	1025	**1112**	1205	1255	**1345**	1435	1530	1710	1025	1255	1530	1025	1255	**1530**	**1150**	**1530**
Tanygrisiau d.	1043	**1135**	1223	1313	**1407**	1458	1548	1728	1043	1313	1548	RQ	RQ	**RQ**	**RQ**	**RQ**
Bl. Ffestiniog a.	1055	**1146**	1233	1325	**1417**	1507	1600	1740	1055	1325	1600	1055	1325	**1600**	**1220**	**1600**
British Rail Conwy Valley line (See notes below) NO SUNDAY SERVICE — Bl. Ffestiniog d.	1105			1330	1450		1625	1748		1330	1625		1330	1625	1330	1625
Llandudno Jcn. a.	1204			1431	1548		1726	1845		1431	1726		1431	1726	1431	1726
Llandudno a.	1214			1441	1558		1736	1903		1441	1736		1441	1736	1441	1736
Llandudno d.	0950		1110			1333	1450	1630	0830	1110	1450	0830	1110	1450	1110	1450
Llandudno Jcn. d.	1000		1121			1343	1501	1640	0840	1121	1501	0840	1121	1501	1121	1501
Bl. Ffestiniog a.	1100		1224			1445	1609	1741	0940	1224	1609	0940	1224	1609	1224	1609
Bl. Ffestiniog d.	1105	**1155**	1245	1340	**1430**	1520	1615	1746	1105	1340	1615	1105	1340	**1615**	**1230**	**1615**
Tanygrisiau d.	1111	**1201**	1251	1346	**1436**	1526	1621	1752	1111	1346	1621	RQ	RQ	**RQ**	**RQ**	**RQ**
Tan-y-Bwlch d.	1133	**1225**	1315	1405	**1500**	1550	1640	1814	1133	1405	1640	1133	1405	**1640**	**1258**	**1640**
Penrhyn d.	1149	**1245**	1335	1424	**1520**	1606	1659	1830	1149	1424	1659	1149	1424	**1659**	**1314**	**1659**
Minffordd d.	1154	**1250**	1340	1429	**1525**	1611	1706	1835	1154	1429	1704	1154	1429	**1704**	**1319**	**1704**
British Rail Cambrian Coast line (See notes below) NO SUNDAY SERVICE — Minffordd d.	1205			1530		1710		1955	1205	1530	1710	1205	1530	1710	1530	1710
Barmouth a.	1246			1616		1751		2033	1246	1616	1751	1246	1616	1751	1616	1751
Minffordd d.			1422		1606		1834	2212	1325	1606	1834	1422	1606	1834	1422	1834
Pwllheli a.			1450		1633		1901	2239	1353	1633	1901	1450	1633	1901	1450	1901
Porthmadog a.	1209	**1304**	1354	1444	**1539**	1625	1719	1848	1207	1442	1717	1207	1442	**1717**	**1332**	**1717**

1 A487 Caernarfon
2 A497 Criccieth & Pwllheli
A498
Beddgelert
Pont Aberglaslyn
Snowdonia National Park
BLAENAU FFESTINIOG
Llechwedd Slate Caverns
A4085
Prenteg
Glaslyn Hotel
Llyn Stwlan
TANYGRISIAU
F.R.
Tremadog
A487
B4410
Garreg
Rhyd
A496
A470
Power Station
R Glaslyn
A4085
B4410
TAN-Y-BWLCH
nature trail
Morfa Bychan
PORTHMADOG
PENRHYN
MINFFORDD
Oakeley Arms Hotel
A487
B4391
F.R.
TOLL
Borth-y-Gest
BOSTON LODGE
Penrhyndeudraeth
R Dwyryd
A496
Ffestiniog
TOLL
A496
A487
B4391
Bala A5
Maentwrog
Portmeirion
A470
Rheilffordd Railway Rheilffordd Railway
Ffestiniog
Rheilffordd Railway Rheilffordd Railway
Trawsfynydd
nuclear power station
A496
A4212 Bala A5
A470 Trawsfynydd & Dolgellau
Harlech and Barmouth

by Narrow Gauge Train through the Mountains of Snowdonia

NOTES

NOTES ON BRITISH RAIL CONNECTING SERVICES

b — until 12 May
c — from 13 May
g — Saturdays 18 May to 28 September, retimed Pwllheli dep. 0838, Minffordd arr. 0911
FO — Fridays only
SO — Saturdays only

British Rail services may b subject to alteration at Ban Holiday periods.

NOTES ON FFESTINIOG RAILWAY SERVICES

1134 1140 1200 1218 1230 denotes DIESEL HAULED TRAINS — 'ECONOMY' FARES AVAILABLE. Considerable reduction for passengers commencing a FULL RETURN JOURNEY by such trains The return journey ma be made by any train.

All other services ar normally steam hauled.

RQ Stops on request only Passengers wishing t alight should inform th guard before boarding. Passengers wishing t join should give a clea handsignal to the driver All trains other than the 0840 ex. Porthmadog wi also call on request a Boston Lodge, Plas and Dduallt.

Every effort possible wil be made to ensure running as timetable bu the Ffestiniog Railway wil not guarantee advertised connections nor the advertised traction in the event of breakdown o other obstruction o services.

Special parties and private charter by arrangement.

Please apply to:
FFESTINIOG RAILWAY
HARBOUR STATION
PORTHMADOG
GWYNEDD
Telephone:
PORTHMADOG
(0766) 2340/2384

FATHER CHRISTMAS EXCURSIONS

A special service will operate on 21 and 22 December. Details available from 1 October.
Father Christmas will meet the trains and distribute presents to the children.
All seats reservable — Advance Booking Essential.

SOLUTIONS TO "THE FFESTINIOG RAILWAY"

The graph below satisfies all the criteria. Two passing places are needed, situated at approximately 4.2 miles and 9.4 miles from Porthmadog. Trains depart from the stations at regular, 50 minutes intervals.

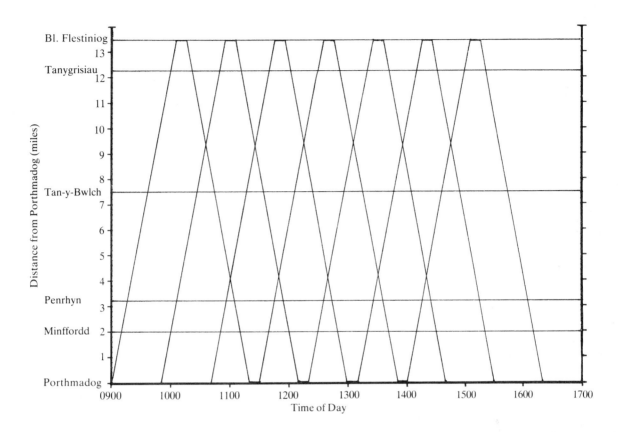

This gives us the following timetable:

Miles	Station		Daily Timetable						
0	Porthmadog	d	09.00	09.50	10.40	11.30	12.20	13.10	14.00
2	Minffordd	d	09.10	10.00	10.50	11.40	12.30	13.20	14.10
3¼	Penrhyn	d	09.15	10.05	10.55	11.45	12.35	13.25	14.15
7½	Tan-y-Bwlch	d	09.35	10.25	11.15	12.05	12.55	13.45	14.35
12¼	Tanygrisiau	d	10.00	10.50	11.40	12.30	13.20	14.10	15.00
13½	Blaenau Ffestiniog	a	10.05	10.55	11.45	12.35	13.25	14.15	15.05
0	Blaenau Ffestiniog	d	10.15	11.05	11.55	12.45	13.35	14.25	15.15
1¼	Tanygrisiau	d	10.20	11.10	12.00	12.50	13.40	14.30	15.20
6	Tan-y-Bwlch	d	10.45	11.35	12.25	13.15	14.05	14.55	15.45
10¼	Penrhyn	d	11.05	11.55	12.45	13.35	14.25	15.15	16.05
11½	Minffordd	d	11.10	12.00	12.50	13.40	14.30	15.20	16.10
13½	Porthmadog	a	11.20	12.10	13.00	13.50	14.40	15.30	16.20

CARBON DATING

Carbon dating is a technique for discovering the age of an ancient object, (such as a bone or a piece of furniture) by measuring the amount of Carbon 14 that it contains.

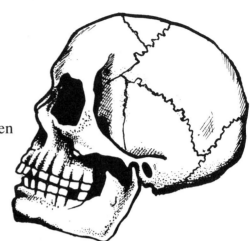

While plants and animals are alive, their Carbon 14 content remains constant, but when they die it decreases to radioactive decay.

The amount, a, of Carbon 14 in an object t thousand years after it dies is given by the formula:

$$a = 15.3 \times 0.886^{\,t}$$

(The quantity "a" measures the rate of Carbon 14 atom disintegrations and this is measured in "counts per minute per gram of carbon (cpm)")

1   Imagine that you have two samples of wood. One was taken from a fresh tree and the other was taken from a charcoal sample found at Stonehenge and is 4000 years old.

   How much Carbon 14 does each sample contain? (Answer in cpm's)

   How long does it take for the amount of Carbon 14 in each sample to be halved?

   These two answers should be the same, (Why?) and this is called the *half-life* of Carbon 14.

2   Charcoal from the famous Lascaux Cave in France gave a count of 2.34 cpm. Estimate the date of formation of the charcoal and give a date to the paintings found in the cave.

3   Bones A and B are x and y thousand years old respectively. Bone A contains three times as much Carbon 14 as bone B.

   What can you say about x and y?

CARBON DATING . . . SOME HINTS

Using a calculator, draw a table of values and plot a graph to show how the amount of Carbon 14 in an object varies with time.

t (1000's of years)	0	1	2	3	4	5	6	7	8	9	10	. . .	17
a (c.p.m)													

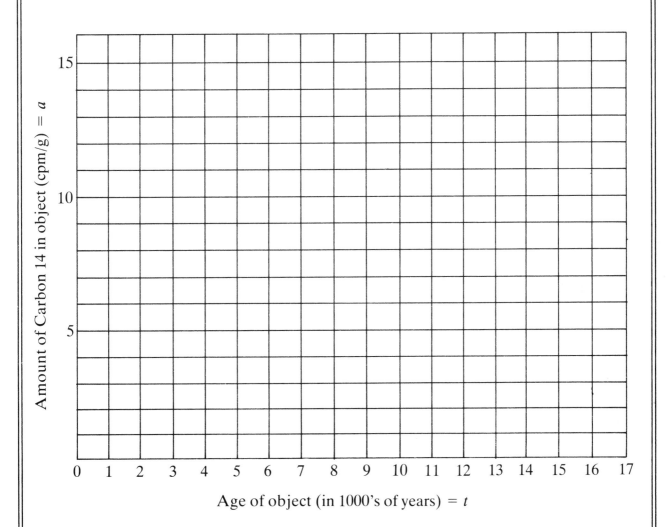

Use your graph to read off answers to the questions.

SOLUTIONS TO "CARBON DATING"

If pupils have difficulty with the exponential notation used in this worksheet, then refer them back to booklet B3, "Looking at exponential functions", where there are similar items in the context of "Hypnotic drugs".

The following table and graph both illustrate how the amount of Carbon 14 in an object decays:

Age of object (1000's of years)	Amount of C14 (cpm/g)	Age of object (1000's of years)	Amount of C14 (cpm/g)
0	15.3	9	5.15
1	13.56	10	4.56
2	12.01	11	4.04
3	10.64	12	3.58
4	9.43	13	3.17
5	8.35	14	2.81
6	7.40	15	2.49
7	6.56	16	2.21
8	5.81	17	1.95

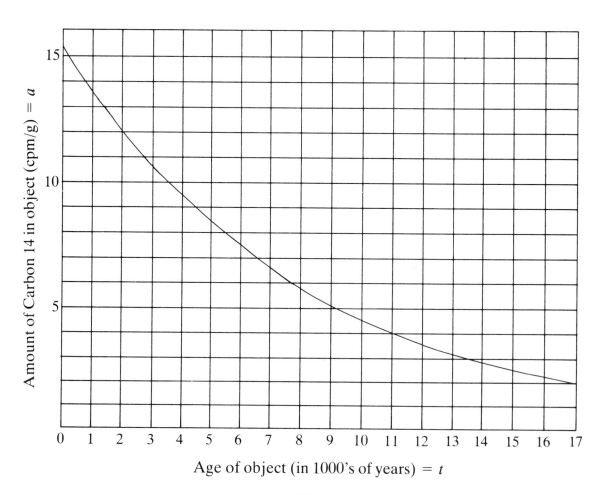

Age of object (in 1000's of years) = t

172

1. The fresh wood will contain 15.3 cpm's of Carbon 14.

    The Stonehenge sample will contain 9.43 cpm's of Carbon 14.

    In each case, the quantity of Carbon 14 will be halved after a further 5,700 years, approximately. (Pupils with no knowledge of logarithms will have to discover this graphically, or numerically by trial and error.)

2. The charcoal from the caves is about 15,500 years old, and so the paintings date back to approximately 13,500 BC.

3. The relationship $y = x + 9$ is approximately true. (In other words, the 'third' life of Carbon 14 is approximately 9 years).

DESIGNING A CAN

A cylindrical can, able to contain half a litre of drink, is to be manufactured from aluminium. The volume of the can must therefore be 500 cm³.

* Find the radius and height of the can which will use the least aluminium, and therefore be the cheapest to manufacture. (i.e., find out how to minimise the surface area of the can).

  State clearly any assumptions you make.

* What shape is your can? Do you know of any cans that are made with this shape? Can you think of any practical reasons why more cans are not this shape?

DESIGNING A CAN ... SOME HINTS

* You are told that the volume of the can must be 500 cm³.

   If you made the can very tall, would it have to be narrow or wide? Why?

   If you made the can very wide, would it have to be tall or short? Why?

   Sketch a *rough* graph to describe how the height and radius of the can have to be related to each other.

* Let the radius of the can be *r* cm, and the height be *h* cm.

   Write down algebraic expressions which give

   — the volume of the can

   — the total surface area of the can, in terms of *r* and *h*.
      (remember to include the two ends!).

* Using the fact that the volume of the can must be 500 cm³, you could
   either: – try to find some possible pairs of values for *r* and *h*
               (do this systematically if you can).

      – for each of your pairs, find out the corresponding surface area.

   or: – try to write one single expression for the surface area in terms of *r*,
            by eliminating *h* from your equations.

* Now plot a graph to show how the surface area varies as *r* is increased, and use your graph to find the value of *r* that minimises this surface area.

* Use your value of *r* to find the corresponding value of *h*. What do you notice about your answers? What shape is the can?

175

SOLUTIONS TO "DESIGNING A CAN"

Most pupils will probably find it more natural to begin by evaluating possible pairs of values for the radius (r cm) and height (h cm) of the can using

$$V = \pi r^2 h = 500 \qquad — \text{①}$$
$$\Leftrightarrow \qquad h = \frac{500}{\pi r^2}$$

and then evaluate the corresponding surface areas using

$$A = 2\pi rh + 2\pi r^2 \qquad — \text{②}$$
$$\Leftrightarrow \qquad A = 2\pi r (r + h)$$

This approach will result in the following kind of table:

r (cm)	0	1	2	3	4	5	6	7	8	9	10
h (cm)	∞	159	39.8	17.7	9.9	6.4	4.4	3.3	2.5	2	1.6
A	∞	1006	525	390	350	357	393	450	527	620	728

A more sophisticated approach with more algebraic manipulation, but less numerical calculation, involves substituting $\pi rh = \frac{500}{r}$ (from ①) into ②, obtaining:

$$A = \frac{1000}{r} + 2\pi r^2$$

(This removes the need to calculate intermediate values for h in the table.)

This table results in the graph shown opposite.

176

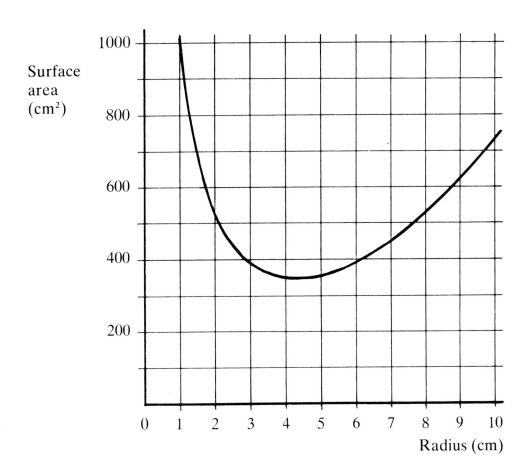

The minimum surface area is therefore approximately 350 cm³ (more exactly, 349 cm³) and this occurs when the radius is 4.3 cm and the height is 8.6 cm. This means that, when viewed from the side, the can is 'square'. (Notice that it makes very little difference to the surface area used if the radius varies between 3 cm and 6 cm.) Narrower cans are much easier to hold and this may partly account for the reason why so few 'square' cans are marketed.

MANUFACTURING A COMPUTER

Imagine that you are running a small business which assembles and sells two kinds of computer: Model A and Model B (the cheaper version). You are only able to manufacture up to 360 computers, of either type, in any given week.

The following table shows all the relevant data concerning the employees at your company:

Job Title	Number of people doing this job	Job description	Pay	Hours worked
Assembler	100	This job involves putting the computers together	£100 per week	36 hours per week
Inspector	4	This job involves testing and correcting any faults in the computers before they are sold	£120 per week	35 hours per week

The next table shows all the relevant data concerning the manufacture of the computers.

	Model A	Model B
Total assembly time in man-hours for each computer	12	6
Total inspection and correction time in man-minutes for each computer	10	30
Component costs for each computer	£80	£64
Selling price for each computer	£120	£88

At the moment, you are manufacturing and selling 100 of Model A and 200 of Model B each week.

*   What profit are you making at the moment?

*   How many of each computer should you make in order to improve this worrying situation?

*   Would it help if you were to make some employees redundant?

MANUFACTURING A COMPUTER ... SOME HINTS

1 Suppose you manufacture 100 Model A's and 200 Model B's in one week:

 * How much do you pay in wages?

 * How much do you pay for components?

 * What is your weekly income?

 * What profit do you make?

2 Now suppose that you manufacture x Model A and y Model B computers each week.

 * Write down 3 inequalities involving x and y. These will include:
   — considering the time it takes to assemble the computers, and the total time that the assemblers have available.
   — considering the time it takes to inspect and correct faults in the computers, and the total time the inspectors have available.

Draw a graph and show the region satisfied by all 3 inequalities:

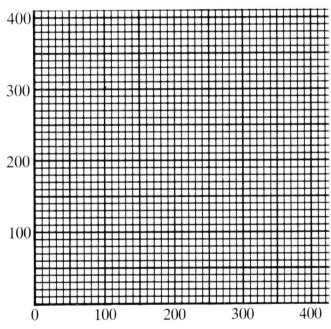

Number of Model B computers manufactured (y)

Number of Model A computers manufactured (x)

3 Work out an expression which tells you the profit made on x Model A and y Model B computers.

4 Which points on your graph maximise your profit?

1 The wage bill per week is   £100 × 100 + £120 × 4 = £10,480

The components bill for 100 Model A's and 200 Model B's is
$$£80 × 100 + £64 × 200 = £20,800$$

The weekly income from selling the computers is
$$£120 × 100 + £88 × 200 = £29,600$$

The overall profit is therefore £29,600 − £20,800 − £10,480 = − £1680

So under the current policy, the business is making a loss of £1680 per week!

2 If x model A and y model B computers are made,
Since only a maximum of 360 computers can be
made each week $x + y \leqslant 360$ (I)

The time taken in hours to assemble the
computers is $12x + 6y$ $12x + 6y \leqslant 3600$
The time available for the assemblers
is $100 × 36 = 3600$ $\Rightarrow 2x + y \leqslant 600$ (II)

The time taken in minutes to inspect
the computers is $10x + 30y$ $10x + 30y \leqslant 8400$
The time in minutes available for
inspection is $4 × 35 × 60 = 8400$ $\Rightarrow x + 3y \leqslant 840$ (III)

In the graph below, we have shaded out the regions we *don't* want:

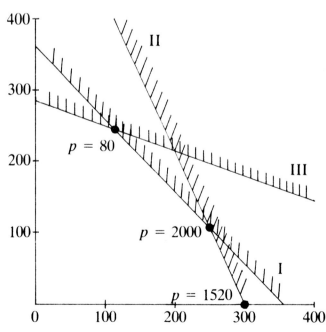

Number
of
Model B
computers
manufactured
(y)

Number of Model A computers manufactured (x)

180

3   The profit £p made on x model A and y model B computers is given by:

$$p = (120x + 88y) - (80x + 64y) - (100 \times 100 - 120 \times 4)$$
$$= 40x + 24y - 10{,}480$$

4   The maximum profit of £2000 per week occurs when 240 Model A and 120 Model B computers are produced each week. (In this case, it is interesting to note that one inspector is not needed. If he or she was made redundant this would increase the profit by a further £120 per week).

THE MISSING PLANET 1.

In our solar system, there are nine major planets, and many other smaller bodies such as comets and meteorites. The five planets nearest to the sun are shown in the diagram below.

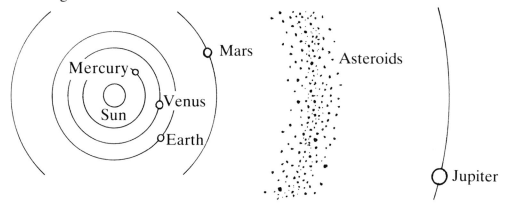

Between Mars and Jupiter lies a belt of rock fragments called the 'asteroids'. These are, perhaps, the remains of a tenth planet which disintegrated many years ago. We shall call this, planet 'X'. In these worksheets, you will try to discover everything you can about planet 'X' by looking at patterns which occur in the other nine planets.

How far was planet 'X' from the sun, before it disintegrated?

The table below compares the distances of some planets from the Sun with that of our Earth. (So, for example, Saturn is 10 times as far away from the Sun as the Earth. Scientists usually write this as 10 A.U. or 10 'Astronomical Units').

* Can you spot any pattern in the sequence of *approximate* relative distances.
* Can you use this pattern to predict the missing figures?
* So how far away do you think planet 'X' was from the Sun? (The Earth is 93 million miles away)
* Check your completed table with the planetary data sheet.
  Where does the pattern seem to break down?

Planet	Relative Distance from Sun, approx (exact figures are shown in brackets)	
Mercury	?	
Venus	0.7	(0.72)
Earth	1	(1)
Mars	1.6	(1.52)
Planet X	?	
Jupiter	5.2	(5.20)
Saturn	10	(9.54)
Uranus	19.6	(19.18)
Neptune	?	
Pluto	?	

PLANETARY DATA SHEET

Planet	Average distance from the Sun. (millions of miles)	Diameter in miles.	Speed at which it flies through Space (mph)	Speed at which a point on the equator spins round (mph)	Time taken to go once round the Sun. (years)	Time taken to spin round once	Number of 'moons'
Earth	93	7 926	66 641	1 040	1	23.9 hours	1
Jupiter	484	88 700	29 216	28 325	11.86	9.9 hours	12
Mars	142	4 217	53 980	538	1.88	24.6 hours	2
Mercury	36	3 032	107 132	7	0.24	58.7 days	0
Neptune	2 794	30 800	12 147	6 039	164.8	15.8 hours	2
Pluto	3 674	3 700	10 604	77	248	6.3 days	0
Saturn	887	74 600	21 565	22 892	29.46	10.2 hours	10
Uranus	1 784	32 200	15 234	9 193	84.02	10.7 hours	5
Venus	67	7 521	78 364	4	0.61	243 days	0

PLUTO

NEPTUNE

URANUS

SATURN

JUPITER

MARS

EARTH

VENUS

MERCURY

SUN

THE MISSING PLANET... SOME BACKGROUND INFORMATION

In 1772, when planetary distances were still only known in relative terms, a German astronomer named David Titius discovered the same pattern as the one you have been looking at. This 'law' was published by Johann Bode in 1778 and is now commonly known as "Bode's Law". Bode used the pattern, as you have done, to *predict* the existence of a planet 2.8 AU from the sun. (2.8 times as far away from the Sun as the Earth) and towards the end of the eighteenth century scientists began to search systematically for it. This search was fruitless until New Year's Day 1801, when the Italian astronomer Guiseppe Piazzi discovered a very small asteroid which he named Ceres at a distance 2.76 AU from the Sun—astonishingly close to that predicted by Bode's Law. (Since that time, thousands of other small asteroids have been discovered, at distances between 2.2 and 3.2 AU from the sun.)

In 1781, Bode's Law was again apparently confirmed, when William Herschel discovered the planet Uranus, orbitting the sun at a distance of 19.2 AU, again startlingly close to 19.6 AU as predicted by Bode's Law. Encouraged by this, other astronomers used the 'law' as a starting point in the search for other distant planets.

However, when Neptune and Pluto were finally discovered, at 30 AU and 39 AU from the Sun, respectively, it was realised that despite its past usefulness, Bode's 'law' does not really govern the design of the solar system.

THE MISSING PLANET 2.

Look at the Planetary data sheet, which contains 7 statistics for each planet.

The following scientists are making hypotheses about the relationship between these statistics:

A The further a planet is away from the Sun, the longer it takes to orbit the Sun.

B Bigger planets have more moons.

C The smaller the planet the slower it spins.

* Do you agree with these hypotheses? How true are they? (Use the data sheet)

* Invent a list of your own hypotheses.
  Sketch a graph to illustrate each of them.

One way to test a hypothesis is to draw a scattergraph. This will give you some idea of how strong the relationship is between the two variables.

For example, here is a 'sketch' scattergraph testing the hypothesis of scientist A:

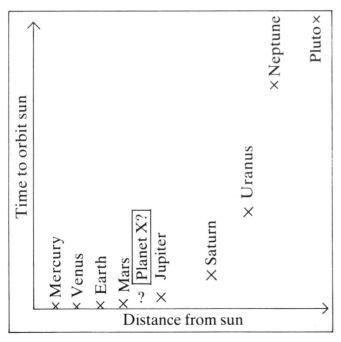

Notice that:

There *does* appear to be a relationship between the distance a planet is from the Sun and the time it takes to orbit once. The hypothesis seems to be confirmed.

We can therefore predict the orbital time for Planet X. It should lie between that of Mars (2 years) and Jupiter (12 years). (A more accurate statement would need a more accurate graph.)

* *Sketch* scattergraphs to test your own hypotheses. What else *can* be found out about Planet X? What *cannot* be found?

THE MISSING PLANET 3.

After many years of observation the famous
mathematician Johann Kepler (1571-1630)
found that the time taken for a planet to orbit
the Sun (T years) and its average distance
from the Sun (R miles) are related by the
formula

$$\frac{R^3}{T^2} = K \qquad \text{where } K \text{ is a constant value.}$$

* Use a calculator to check this formula from the data sheet, and find the value
  of K.

  Use your value of K to find a more accurate estimate for the orbital time (T)
  of Planet X. (You found the value of R for Planet X on the first of these
  sheets).

* We asserted that the orbits of planets are 'nearly circular'. Assuming this is
  so, can you find another formula which connects

  — The average distance of the planet from the Sun (R miles)

  — The time for one orbit (T years)

  — The speed at which the planet 'flies through space' (V miles per hour)?

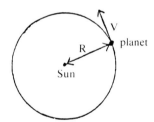

(Hint: Find out how far the planet
moves during one orbit. You can
write this down in two different
ways using R, T and V)
(Warning: T is in *years*, V is in
miles per *hour*)

Use a calculator to check your formula from the data sheet.
Use your formula, together with what you already know about R and T, to
find a more accurate estimate for the speed of Planet X.

* Assuming that the planets are spherical, can you find a relationship
  connecting

  — The diameter of a planet (d miles)

  — The speed at which a point on the equator spins (v miles
  per hour)

  — The time the planet takes to spin round once (t hours)?

Check your formula from the data sheet.

SOLUTIONS TO "THE MISSING PLANET"

Sheet 1

The following pattern may be used to predict the relative distances of the various planets to the sun:

0.55   0.7   1   1.6   2.8   5.2   10   19.6   38.8   77.2

+0.15   +0.3   +0.6   +1.2   +2.4   +4.8   +9.6   +19.2   +38.4

This pattern predicts that Planet X is 2.8 × 93 million miles (= 260.4 million miles) from the sun. The background information sheet describes how this pattern was originally used to predict the positions of asteroids and other planets.

The actual, more precise sequence is:

0.39, 0.72, 1, 1.52, 2.9, 5.20, 9.54, 19.18, 30.1, 39.5.

This shows that the pattern seems to break down for Mercury, Neptune and Pluto. It is interesting to note that if there was no Neptune then the pattern would fit more closely.

Sheet 2

Scientist A is making a statement which is always true.
Scientist B is making a statement which is often true.
Scientist C is making a statement which is never true.

If we denote the 7 variables on the data sheet by R, d, V, v, T, t, and m respectively, then there will be strong correlations within the group of variables R, V and T and within the group d, v and t, but no correllations between members of the different groups. Variable m does not correllate strongly with any other variable.

We have only found data concerning R for planet X. The scattergraph method will therefore only produce additional information regarding V and T.

Sheet 3

From the data sheet, it can be seen that for every planet

$$\frac{R^3}{T^2} = 8.06 \times 10^{23} \ (\pm \ 0.5\%)$$

Where R = the average distance from a planet to the sun in miles
and T = the time taken for a planet to orbit the sun in years

Using 260.4 million miles (= 2.604×10^8 miles) as the estimated distance of planet X, we obtain its orbital period as

$$T = \sqrt{\frac{(2.604 \times 10^8)^3}{8.06 \times 10^{23}}} = 4.68 \text{ years or } \textit{4 years 8 months}$$

(The working would have been easier if R was taken to be in *millions* of miles, giving k as 806000)

Assuming that the planetary orbits are nearly circular, then we obtain:

$$C = 2\pi R$$
$$C = 8760VT$$

where C = circumference of one orbit in miles

V = speed at which a planet moves through space in miles per hour.

(The figure 8760 is a conversion factor from miles per hour to miles per year.)

One way of checking these formula from the data sheet is by evaluating $\dfrac{8760VT}{2\pi R}$
for each planet. If the orbits are circular we should then find out that our answers are all equal to unity. (In fact we find that the values have a mean of about 0.998).

The speed of planet X can now be found by substituting $T = 4.68$, $R = 2.604 \times 10^8$ into

$$V = \frac{2\pi R}{8760T} \simeq 40{,}000 \text{ (mph)}$$

Assuming that the planets are spherical, then we should find that
$$\pi d = vt$$
where d = diameter of the planet

v = speed at which a point on the equator spins

t = time for the planet to rotate once

This checks quite nicely with the information presented on the data sheet.

GRAPHS AND OTHER DATA FOR INTERPRETATION

The following section contains a miscellaneous collection of shorter situations which are intended to provide additional practice at interpreting data.

We hope that this material will provide you with a useful resource which can be dipped into from time to time. Solutions have not been provided for this section.

FEELINGS

These graphs show how a girl's feelings varied during a typical day.

Her timetable for the day was as follows:

7.00 am	woke up
8.00 am	went to school
9.00 am	Assembly
9.30 am	Science
10.30 am	Break
11.00 am	Maths
12.00 am	Lunchtime
1.30 pm	Games
2.45 pm	Break
3.00 pm	French
4.00 pm	went home
6.00 pm	did homework
7.00 pm	went 10-pin bowling
10.30 pm	went to bed

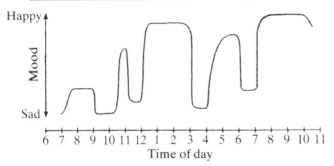

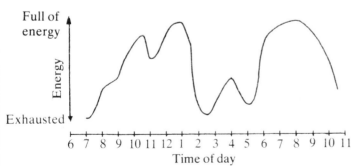

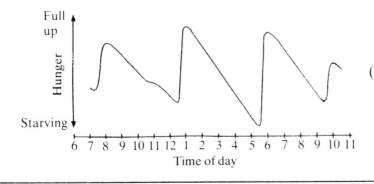

(a) Try to explain the shape of each graph, as fully as possible.

(b) How many meals did she eat?
Which meal was the biggest?
Did she eat at breaktimes?
How long did she spend eating lunch?
Which lesson did she enjoy the most?
When was she "tired and depressed?" Why was this?
When was she "hungry but happy?" Why was this?

Make up some more questions like these, and give them to your neighbour to solve.

(c) Sketch graphs to show how *your* feelings change during the day. See if your neighbour can interpret them correctly.

THE TRAFFIC SURVEY

A survey was conducted to discover the volume of traffic using a particular road. The results were published in the form of the graph which shows the number of cars using the road at any specified time during a typical Sunday and Monday in June.

1. Try to explain, as fully as possible, the shape of the graph.

2. Compare Sunday's graph with Monday's. What is suprising?

3. Where do you think this road could be? (Give an example of a road you know of, which may produce such a graph.)

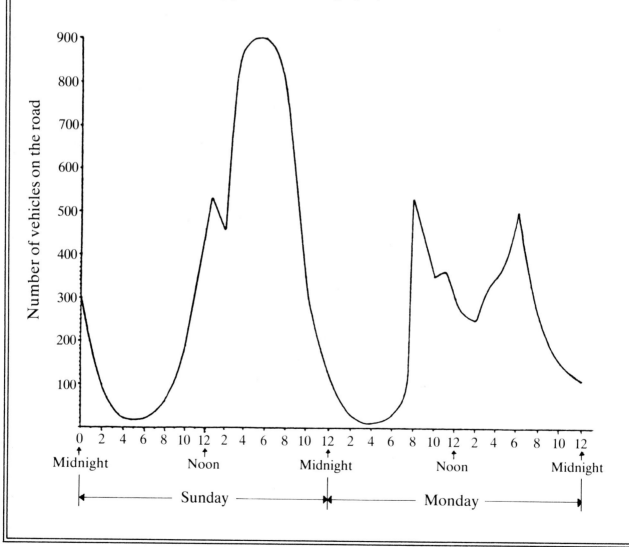

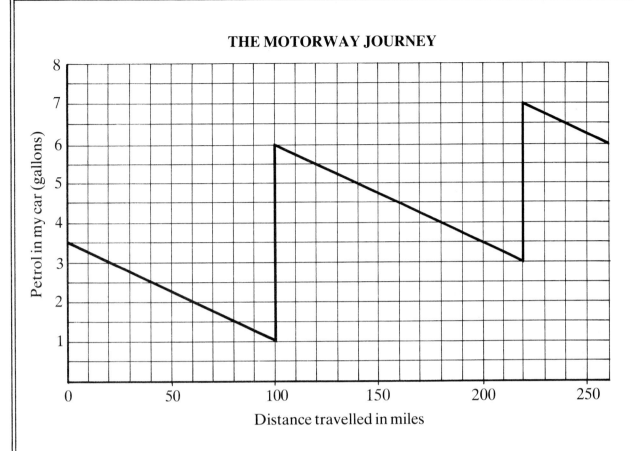

THE MOTORWAY JOURNEY

Petrol in my car (gallons) (y-axis)

Distance travelled in miles (x-axis)

The above graph shows how the amount of petrol in my car varied during a motorway journey.

Write a paragraph to explain the shape of the graph. In particular answer the following questions:

1   How much petrol did I have in my tank after 130 miles?
2   My tank holds about 9 gallons. Where was it more than half full?
3   How many petrol stations did I stop at?
4   At which station did I buy the most petrol? How can you tell?
5   If I had not stopped anywhere, where would I have run out of petrol?
6   If I had only stopped once for petrol, where would I have run out?
7   How much petrol did I use for the first 100 miles?
8   How much petrol did I use over the entire journey?
9   How many miles per gallon (mpg) did my car do on this motorway?

I left the motorway, after 260 miles, I drove along country roads for 40 miles and then 10 miles through a city, where I had to keep stopping and starting. Along country roads, my car does about 30 mpg, but in the city it's more like 20 mpg.

10   Sketch a graph to show the remainder of my journey.

GROWTH CURVES

Paul and Susan are two fairly typical people. The following graphs compare how their weights have changed during their first twenty years.

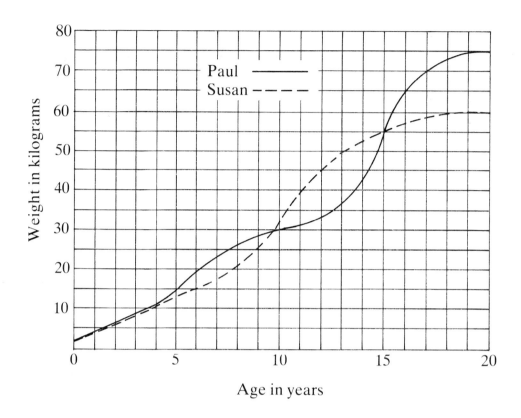

Write a paragraph comparing the shape of the two graphs. Write down everything you think is important.

Now answer the following:

1 How much weight did each person put on during their "secondary school" years (between the ages of 11 and 18)?

2 When did Paul weigh more than Susan? How can you tell?

3 When did they both weigh the same?

4 When was Susan putting on weight most rapidly?
   How can you tell this from the graph?
   How fast was she growing at this time? (Answer in kg per year).

5 When was Paul growing most rapidly? How fast was he growing at this time?

6 Who was growing faster at the age of 14? How can you tell?

7 When was Paul growing faster than Susan?

8 Girls tend to have boyfriends older than themselves. Why do you think this is so? What is the connection with the graph?

ROAD ACCIDENT STATISTICS

The following four graphs show how the number of road accident casualties per hour varies during a typical week.

Graph A shows the normal pattern for Monday, Tuesday, Wednesday and Thursday.

* Which graphs correspond to Friday, Saturday and Sunday?

* Explain the reasons for the shape of each graph, as fully as possible.

* What evidence is there to show that alcohol is a major cause of road accidents?

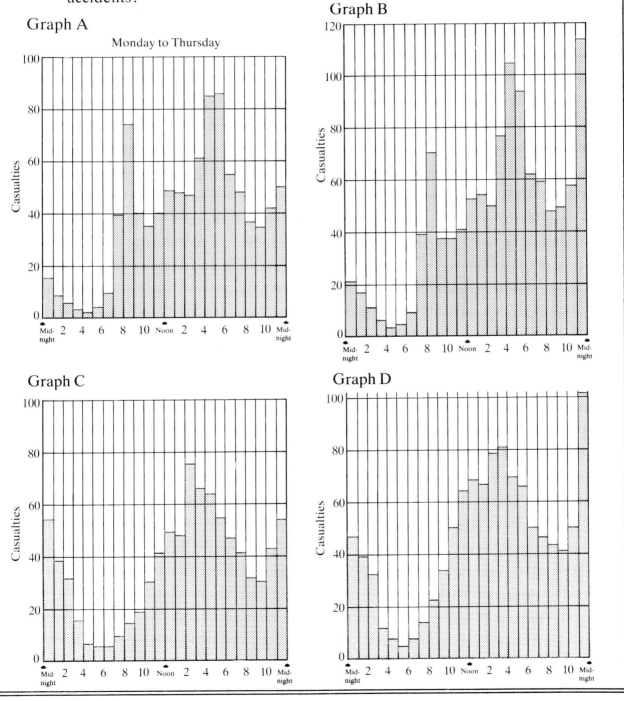

Graph A
Monday to Thursday

Graph B

Graph C

Graph D

THE HARBOUR TIDE

The graph overleaf, shows how the depth of water in a harbour varies on a particular Wednesday.

1   Write a paragraph which describes in detail what the graph is saying:

> When is high/low tide? When is the water level rising/falling?
>
> When is the water level rising/falling most rapidly?
>
> How fast is it rising/falling at this time?
>
> What is the average depth of the water? How much does the depth vary from the average?

2   Ships can only enter the harbour when the water is deep enough. What factors will determine when a particular boat can enter or leave the harbour?

The ship in the diagram below has a draught of 5 metres when loaded with cargo and only 2 metres when unloaded.

Discuss when it can safely enter and leave the harbour.

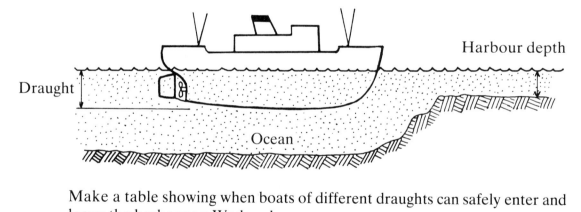

Make a table showing when boats of different draughts can safely enter and leave the harbour on Wednesday.

3   Try to complete the graph in order to predict how the tide will vary on Thursday. How will the table you draw up in question 2 need to be adjusted for Thursday? Friday? ...

4   Assuming that the formula which fits this graph is of the form
$$d = A + B \cos(28t + 166)°$$
(Where d = depth of water in metres
t = time in hours after midnight on Tuesday night)

Can you find out the values of A and B?
How can you do this without substituting in values for t?

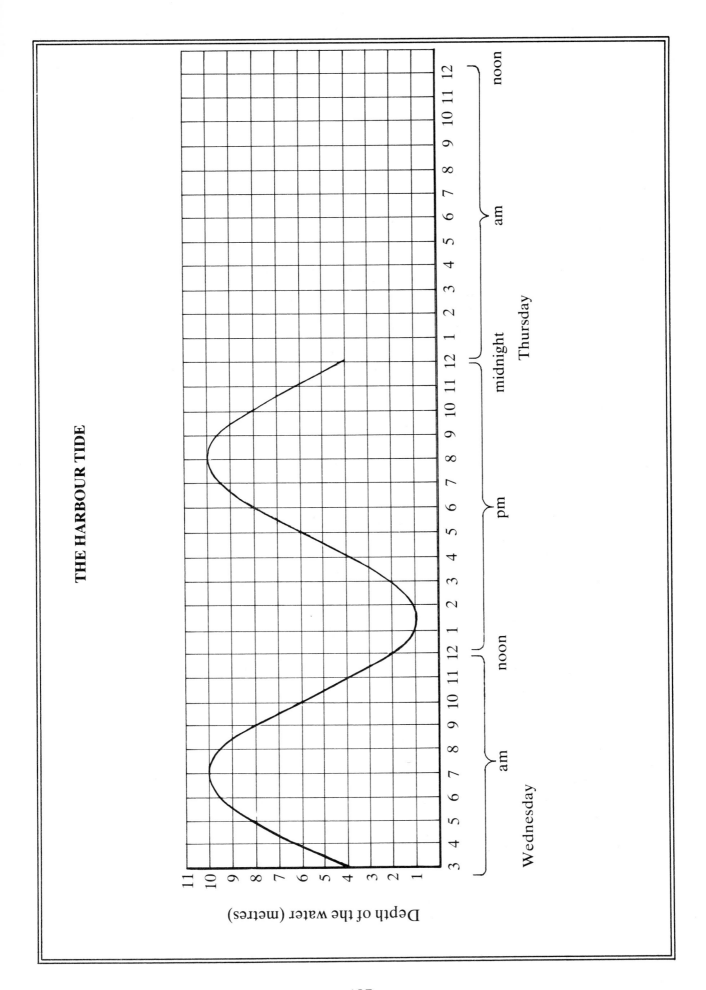

THE HARBOUR TIDE

Depth of the water (metres)

ALCOHOL

Read through the data sheet carefully, and then try to answer the following questions:

> Using the chart and diagram on page 2, describe and compare the effects of consuming different quantities of different drinks.
> (eg: Compare the effect of drinking a pint of beer with a pint of whisky)
> Note that 20 fl oz = 4 gills = 1 pint.
> Illustrate your answer with a table of some kind.

> An 11 stone man leaves a party at about 2 am after drinking 5 pints of beer. He takes a taxi home and goes to bed. Can he legally drive to work at 7 am the next morning? When would you advise him that he is fit to drive? Explain your reasoning as carefully as possible.

The five questions below will help you to compare and contrast the information presented on the data sheet.

1   *Using only the information presented in words by the "Which?" report,*
    draw an accurate graph showing the effect of drinking 5 pints of beer at 2 am.
    a)   What will the blood alcohol level rise to?
    b)   How long will it take to reach this level?
    c)   How quickly will this level drop?
    d)   What is the legal limit for car drivers? How long will this person remain unfit to drive? Explain your reasoning.

2   *Using only the formula provided,*
    draw another graph to show the effect of drinking 5 pints of beer.
    How does this graph differ from the graph produced above?
    Use your formula to answer 1a) b) c) d) again.
    Compare your answers with those already obtained.

3   *Using only the table of data from the AA book of driving,*
    draw another graph to show the effect of an *11 stone* man drinking 5 pints of beer.

    Compare this graph to those already obtained.

    Answer 1a) b) c) d) from this graph, and compare your answers with those above.

198

ALCOHOL... DATA SHEET

Alcohol is more easily available today, and more is drunk, than at any time over the past 60 years. At parties, restaurants and pubs you will be faced with the decision of how much to drink. Hundreds of thousands of people suffer health and social problems because they drink too much, so we feel you should know some facts.

What happens to alcohol in the body?

Most of it goes into the bloodstream. The exact amount will depend on how much has been drunk, whether the stomach is empty or not, and the weight of the person. We measure this amount by seeing how much alcohol (in milligrams) is present in 100 millilitres of blood.

How does alcohol affect behaviour?

You cannot predict the effect of alcohol very accurately, since this will depend on how much you drink, and on your personality. Some people become noisy and others sleepy. Alcohol will affect your judgement, self control and skills (like driving a car).

1

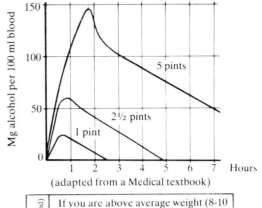

(adapted from a Medical textbook)

Consumption (mg alcohol/100 ml blood)	If you are above average weight (8-10 stone) subtract an hour; below it, add an hour.							
	After 1 Hour	After 2 Hours	After 3 Hours	After 4 Hours	After 5 Hours	After 6 Hours	After 7 Hours	After 8 Hours
15	0	0	0	0	0	0	0	0
30	15	0	0	0	0	0	0	0
45	45	30	15	0	0	0	0	0
60	60	45	30	15	0	0	0	0
75	75	75	60	45	30	15	0	0
90	90	90	75	60	45	30	15	0
105	105	105	90	75	60	45	30	15
120	120	120	105	90	75	60	45	30
135	135	135	135	120	105	90	75	60
150	150	150	150	135	120	105	90	75
165	165	165	165	165	150	135	120	105
180	180	180	180	180	165	150	135	120
195	195	195	195	195	180	165	150	135
210	210	210	210	210	210	195	180	165

(adapted from the A.A. Book of Driving)

4

Draught Bitter 1 pint — 30
Cider ½ pint — 20
Export Lager ½ pint — 20
whisky ⅙ gill — 15
brandy ⅙ gill — 15
sherry 2 fl oz — 20
table wine 4 fl oz — 15

The figures below the glasses show the concentration of alcohol in the blood (in mg per 100 ml) after drinking the measure quoted.

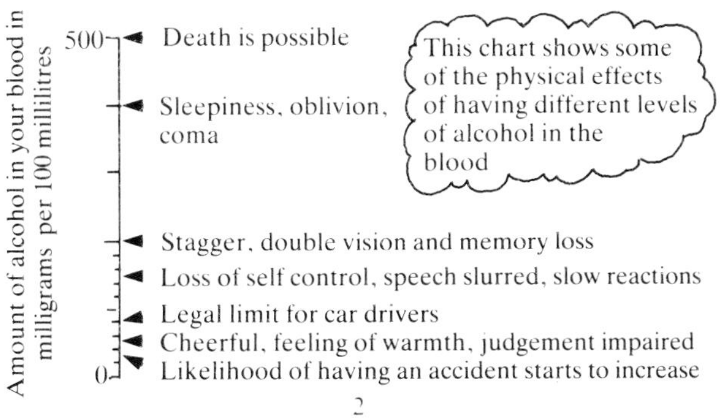

Amount of alcohol in your blood in milligrams per 100 millilitres

500 — Death is possible

— Sleepiness, oblivion, coma

This chart shows some of the physical effects of having different levels of alcohol in the blood

— Stagger, double vision and memory loss
— Loss of self control, speech slurred, slow reactions
— Legal limit for car drivers
— Cheerful, feeling of warmth, judgement impaired
0 — Likelihood of having an accident starts to increase

2

Experts generally agree that a person who regularly drinks more than 4 pints of beer a day (or the equivalent in other forms of drink) is running a high risk of damaging his health. However, smaller amounts than this may still be harmful.

How do the effects of drinking wear off?

The information shown below was taken from four different sources. Do they agree with each other?

Clearly there's an urgent need for more public education about this. Here is a rough guide. An 11 stone man normally raises his blood/alcohol level by about 30mg/100ml with each drink (pint of beer, 2 glasses of wine, or double measure of spirits). So after 2½ such drinks he will probably be just below the legal limit (if he eats a meal at the same time, he may be able to go up to, say, three drinks without going over the limit).

It takes about an hour for the blood/alcohol level to reach a peak. After this time-assuming you've stopped drinking-the blood/alcohol level starts to fall at the rate of about 15mg/100ml (half a drink) per hour. This means that the rate at which you drink is important. For example, your blood/alcohol level will probably be higher after drinking 2½ pints of beer in quick succession than after 4 pints taken over an evening.

Don't look on the 80mg/100ml as a target to aim just short of. Many people (particularly the young) aren't safe to drive at levels well below this, and virtually everyone's reactions are at least slightly slower by the time the blood/alcohol limit approaches 80mg/100ml. For safety's sake you shouldn't drive if your blood/alcohol level is likely to be 50mg/100ml or more. And bear in mind that, after a night's heavy drinking, you may still be unsafe to drive (and over the legal limit) the next morning. Note also that it's an offence to drive or be in charge of a car while 'unfit through drink'-for which you could be convicted even if your blood/alcohol level is below 80mg/100ml

(from a "Which?" report on alcohol).

Let the amount of alcohol in the blood at any time be a mg/100ml.
Let the number of beers drunk be b
Let the number of hours that have passed since the drinking took place be h hours.

Then $a = 30b - 15h + 15$

3

4 *Compare the graph taken from the Medical textbook* with those drawn for questions 1, 2 and 3. Answer question 1a) b) c) and d) concerning the 11 stone man from this graph.

5 Compare the advantages and disadvantages of each mode of representation: words, formula, graph and table, using the following criteria:

Compactness	(does it take up much room?)
Accuracy	(is the information over-simplified?)
Simplicity	(is it easy to understand?)
Versatility	(can it show the effects of drinking different amounts of alcohol easily?)
Reliability	(which set of data do you trust the most? Why? Which set do you trust the least? Why?)

A business woman drinks a glass of sherry, two glasses of table wine and a double brandy during her lunch hour, from 1 pm to 2 pm. Three hours later, she leaves work and joins some friends for a meal, where she drinks two double whiskies.

Draw a graph to show how her blood/alcohol level varied during the entire afternoon (from noon to midnight). When would you have advised her that she was unfit to drive?

Support
Materials

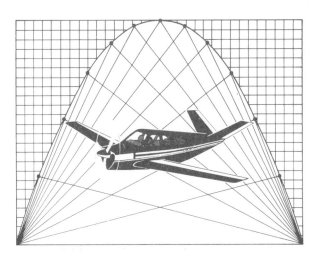

Support Materials

CONTENTS

INTRODUCTION

The following support materials offer a range of ideas, discussion points and activities based on the Module. They can be used by individuals, but it is perhaps more profitable to use them as a basis for a series of meetings with colleagues where classroom experiences may be shared.

This Module, 'The Language of Functions and Graphs', as its title suggests, focuses on communication skills. Pupils are expected to translate contextual information into various mathematical forms (graphs, tables, formulae etc), translate between them, and also interpret them back into the situational context. The main advantage of using graphs, tables or formulae is that they can distil a wealth of information into a small amount of space, and comparatively small changes in them can represent significant changes in meaning. Unfortunately, this 'denseness' of information can also make them difficult to interpret. Most teachers would agree that the ability to interpret and use these modes of information is of importance to pupils of all ages and abilities and many other areas of the school curriculum, such as biology and geography, use graphs and tables extensively.

In order to develop interpretative skills, pupils need many opportunites to talk through their ideas and misconceptions, present evidence and discuss explanations. To some pupils this will be a new way of approaching mathematics and it is worthwhile explaining this to the class before starting on the Module. In fact, a discussion on "how to discuss" can make a valuable introduction to the work. (An example of one teacher's approach is given in Section 3 on page 220).

Language skills play an important role throughout the work. The building up of these skills is only achievable if the individual is actively involved; this is well illustrated by Clive Sutton's diagram below, taken from 'Communicating in the Classroom'.*

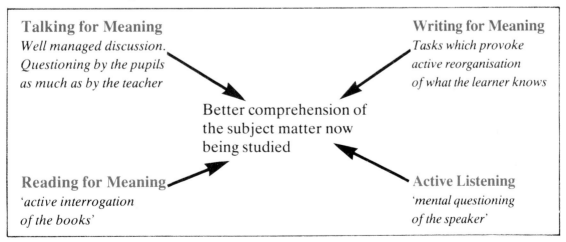

Talking for Meaning
Well managed discussion.
Questioning by the pupils
as much as by the teacher

Writing for Meaning
Tasks which provoke
active reorganisation
of what the learner knows

Better comprehension of
the subject matter now
being studied

Reading for Meaning
'active interrogation
of the books'

Active Listening
'mental questioning
of the speaker'

*'Communicating in the Classroom' edited by Clive Sutton, and published by Hodder and Stoughton, London 1981.
ISBN 0 340 26659 7

It is useful to distinguish two uses for language:

* **Language for telling others** — being able to communicate verbally or diagrammatically so that another person understands;

* **Language for oneself** (or language for learning) — "the struggle to communicate what you want to say is one of the most powerful provocations to sorting out what you understand."

This latter use of language involves the learner in a great deal of active reflection in which she reorganises her own thoughts as she tries to communicate with others. The advantages of encouraging this approach in the classroom is summarised in the following table, which is again taken from the introduction to Sutton (1981):

---

1 **Knowledge reformulated by the learner for himself** is
(a) more easily recalled,
(b) linked to other knowledge, and so accessible from other points in his thought patterns,
(c) more easily *used* in daily living, or when solving a problem, in some other field of thought,
(d) influential upon future perceptions, and an aid to further learning in the subject.

2 **Knowledge that the learner does not reformulate** is
(a) more easily forgotten,
(b) usually remembered only in situations very like those where it was learned,
(c) not applied or used elsewhere.

3 **Reformulation may be provoked**
(a) by small group discussion (in appropriate circumstances),
(b) by any writing which is the pupil's own composition, as long as pupils and teachers *expect* such reformulation, and the relationships between them allow it and encourage it.

The materials in the Module are written with the objective of provoking reformulation of the children's ideas about graphs etc; classroom lessons typically include the following sequence of activities:

i) **A short introductory discussion** aimed at introducing the material, and at equipping pupils with the right expectations. (This includes establishing the relationship referred to in 3(b) above.)

ii) **Pupils working in pairs or small groups.** Here, they may explore the task, consult and discuss with each other, work towards a group consensus and perhaps present their findings to other groups. (This relates to 3(a) above.)

iii) **A 'reporting back' session,** with the teacher chairing or facilitating a whole class discussion, is often appropriate. (This large discussion can also provoke reformulation, so we would include it under 3 above.)

iv) **A 'summing up'** of the current state of knowledge. This may leave the situation still open for further discussion but an attempt should be made to ensure that pupils feel secure in the knowledge that they are heading in the right direction. (It is also useful to look back at the experiences gathered in previous lessons.)

Thus the classroom materials introduce new concepts for the children to understand and at the same time suggest ways of working that may be new to both teachers and pupils. These support materials offer some ideas and comments both on the mathematical concepts and on the range of teaching styles that may be adopted. The suggested activities include working in small groups, exploring microcomputer programs and using the videotape to discuss how others work with the materials. However, if it's not possible to set up such activities we hope that merely reading these support materials will be of help.

These support materials are divided into 5 sections:

Section 1   Tackling a problem in a group

Here, three activities are given that provide teachers with an opportunity to gain personal experience of tackling problems in a small group and then sharing their ideas with a larger group.

Section 2   Children's misconceptions and errors

This section contains a discussion of common difficulties and misconceptions that pupils have experienced with the work on functions and graphs. (In the classroom materials, various worksheets are specifically written to bring these difficulties and misconceptions to light and they are clearly referenced in this section.)

Section 3   Ways of working in the classroom

This section considers the need to balance classroom activities between teacher exposition, small group discussion and class discussion.

Section 4   How can the micro help?

The four programs BRIDGES, SUNFLOWER, BOTTLES and TRAFFIC are briefly described. Activities are suggested to help staff to get to know them.

Section 5   Assessing the examination questions

This section brings us back to assessing children's responses to a few possible examination questions. We show how marking schemes may be devised for other questions and then provide an outine for a practical session using pupils' scripts. (These are included in the 'Masters for Photocopying' pack).

The videotape accompanying this book gives you an opportunity to watch others working with the classroom materials. It shows various ways of working and raises many questions as you see other teachers discussing their experiences. It is worth emphasising that every teacher develops his or her own personal style of working and the teachers that are sharing their methods with us through the video would not wish these extracts to be regarded as 'the way' for everyone to operate. However, they do provide a good focus for a discussion on how the teaching materials may best be used to help children 'think for themselves'.

Finally, as the Cockcroft Report* says:

> "Mathematics teaching at all levels should include opportunities for discussion between teacher and pupils and between pupils themselves."

These support materials attempt to address this recommendation.

---

* 'Mathematics Counts', Report of the Cockcroft Committee of Inquiry into the Teaching of Mathematics, HMSO 1982.

1 TACKLING A PROBLEM IN A GROUP

The Module suggests that children tackle the various worksheets in pairs or in small groups. Effective group discussion is an art that will need gradual development with encouragement and guidance from the teacher.

The activities which follow have been used by teachers to gain more personal experience of how it feels to tackle a problem in a group and then report back to other groups. You might like to try them with a few colleagues, initially working in groups of two or three.

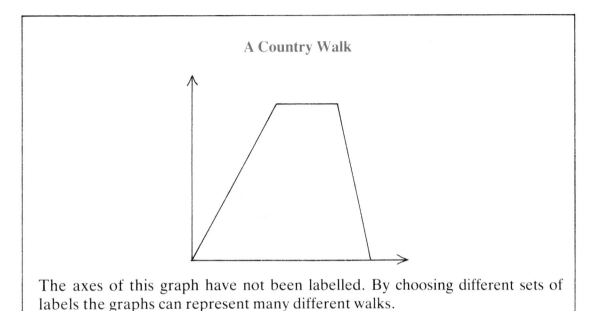

A Country Walk

The axes of this graph have not been labelled. By choosing different sets of labels the graphs can represent many different walks.

Activity 1

(If possible tape record some of your group discussions and analyse them later on).

The first activity is to decide on 5 different country walks that could be illustrated by the given graph. For example, one set of labels could be 'distance from home' for the vertical axis and 'time from the start' for the horizontal axis. A second set of labels could be 'anxiety level' against 'hunger', and so on. For each idea, copy the graph as above, label the axes, name the walk and then write a short description of the particular country walk that the graph is illustrating.

For example:

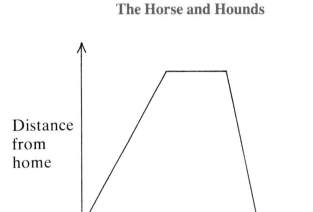

The Horse and Hounds

Distance from home

Time

We set out from home and walked steadily for quite a while. At last we arrived at The Horse and Hounds, it was good to sit in the garden and enjoy a well-earned rest and a few pints of beer. Time passed and we suddenly realised we would have to hurry home if we wanted to arrive before dark — we were anxious not to be away too long because of the baby.

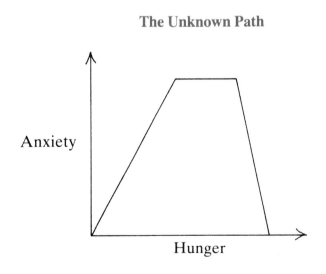

The Unknown Path

Anxiety

Hunger

We had quite a difficult route to follow and it was not easy to pick out the various landmarks. We got more and more worried but after a while Claude noticed that the distant hill must be Beacon's Hang so we hoped we were on the right route. The way became more familiar and we were sure we were on the right path. Unfortunately, we had forgotten to bring our sandwiches.

When you have completed the five descriptions try Activity 2.

Activity 2

Set up a matrix with five columns headed with the names of your five walks and with the five rows labelled with the axes that you chose for each walk (see the example below). The five cells on the leading diagonal will contain the original graph. Copy these onto your matrix. Now, in any order that you find convenient, draw, if possible, a graph using a description of the walk given by the column heading for your information and labelling the axes of the graph as indicated by the row of the matrix. Thus in the example you see in cell (1,2) we have a graph for our 'Unknown Path' walk drawn where the axes are labelled 'Distance from home' against 'Time'. Note any extra assumptions you make in order to complete any cell of the matrix. Once all twenty five cells have been dealt with, turn to Activity 3.

Labels on Axes	Walk 1 The Horse and Hounds	Walk 2 The Unknown Path	Walk 3	Walk 4	Walk 5
Distance from home against Time					
Anxiety against Hunger					

*Many other graphs are possible!

209

Activity 3

The final activity involves reporting your ideas and solutions back to the other groups. Keep any tape recordings you were able to make — they may be analysed later as described in Section 3, pages 221-226. Some general questions may however emerge immediately:

1. Would you have preferred to think about the activities yourself before discussing them with your group?

2. How did the group get organised . . .

    i) . . .to record their decisions?

    ii) . . .to prepare their presentation for the other groups?

3. What role did each member of the group play in the discussion?

    Did anyone . . .

    . . . dominate?

    . . . work independently from the others?

    . . . ask a lot of questions?

    . . . offer suggestions?

    . . . take up or challenge suggestions offered by others?

4. How was the feedback session organised—did each group get a chance to explain its findings?

2   CHILDREN'S MISCONCEPTIONS AND ERRORS

Below we examine some common misconceptions and errors exhibited by children as they work through the Module. Our research evidence* appears to support the view that teaching styles which involve discussing common errors with children are more effective than styles which avoid exposing errors wherever possible. In this Module we have adopted this view and the teaching material is therefore designed to confront rather than avoid the more common areas of difficulty.

1.   **Interpreting a graph as if it were a picture of the situation**

Look at the following example of 'Susan's'

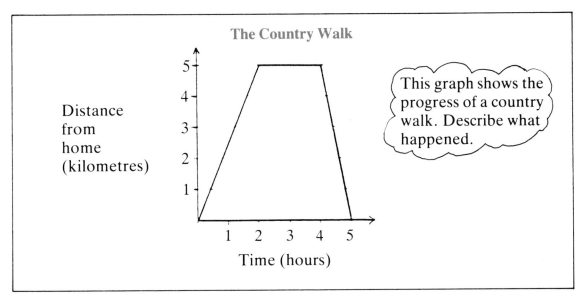

The people on the country walk were walking up a very steep hill. When they finally got to the top they were walking quite slow because they were tired. They carried on walking for a bit and then they went back down the hill on the other side. As they were going down they went at quite a speed.

---

*See for example "Teaching Decimal Place Value — a comparative study of 'Conflict' and 'Positive Only' approaches" by Malcolm Swan, Shell Centre, Nottingham University, 1983. ISBN 0 9061216 010.

211

Susan has interpreted the graph as if it were just a picture of a hill. She has misinterpreted the slope of the graph as indicating the 'steepness of the hill' and this has become confused with her other interpretation involving speed. This kind of misconception is extremely common, and accounts for a very large proportion of errors in interpretation.

Pupils (and even adults) who have become much more sophisticated in interpreting complex graphs can also fall into this kind of error from time to time. The following tasks are taken from A5, "Filling Bottles":

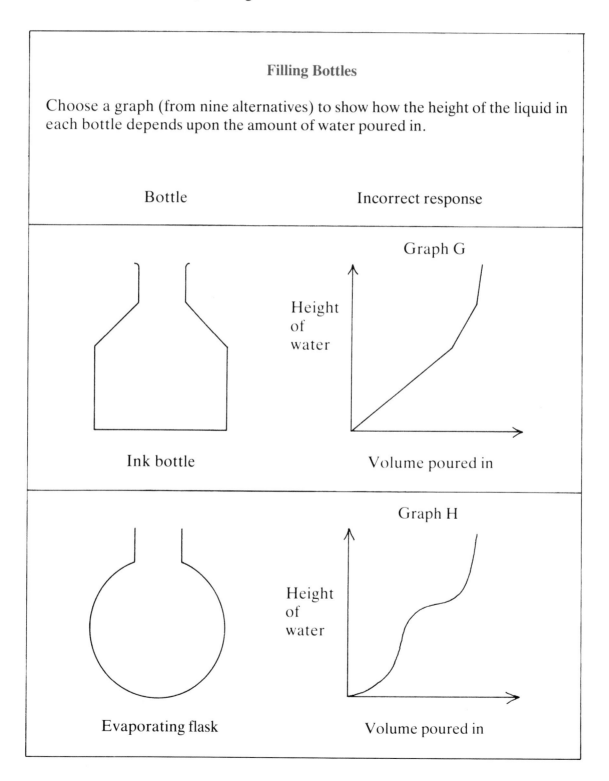

Filling Bottles

Choose a graph (from nine alternatives) to show how the height of the liquid in each bottle depends upon the amount of water poured in.

Bottle   Incorrect response

Graph G

Height of water

Ink bottle   Volume poured in

Graph H

Height of water

Evaporating flask   Volume poured in

In the first of these examples, the pupil has chosen graph G, perhaps assuming that a 'straight' edge on the bottle will always produce a 'straight' line on the graph. It is often difficult to explain why this is not true. In the latter case, the pupil has possibly chosen graph H because he identifies the concave curve on the lower part of the evaporating flask with the concave curve on the lower part of the graph.

This Module enables you to consider this kind of misconception in some depth (Worksheet A2 focuses on it in particular). It will undoubtedly recur in many other guises.

2.   **Answering items which depend on two or more variables**

Consider the following item which is taken from the supplementary booklets at the end of section A (Page 100).

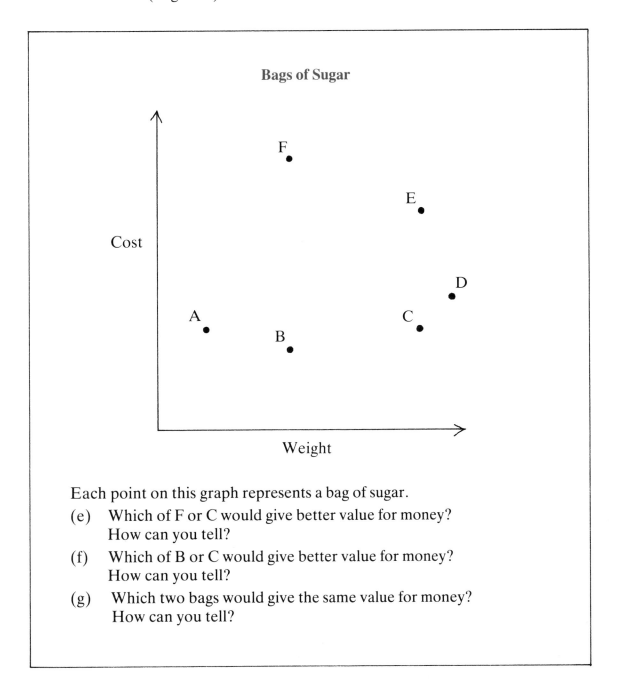

Each point on this graph represents a bag of sugar.
  (e)   Which of F or C would give better value for money?
           How can you tell?
  (f)   Which of B or C would give better value for money?
           How can you tell?
  (g)   Which two bags would give the same value for money?
           How can you tell?

Some pupils find it difficult to consider both variables equally, and often answer the questions as though they depend on just one variable.

Leonard

(e) C. C is less money.

(f) B. Because it is lower in price.

(g) A,C. they beoth the same weight and price

Abby

(e) C because C is heavey and dos'nt cost as much as F.

(f) C because C ways more

(g) E,C because they both way the same.

Both Leonard and Abby are aware of both variables, but while Leonard focuses mainly on the price, Abby focuses mainly on the weight. These questions are quite demanding, and pupils need to adopt some kind of proportional reasoning in order to answer them correctly, for example:

Summi

(f) C. C weighs about 2 times as much as B but cost a little bt more

214

The teaching material within the Module offers a number of items which require such reasoning. In the "Telephone Calls" item in Worksheet A1, for example, pupils have to relate the cost and the duration of a call to the distance over which it is made. (One cannot conclude that because a call is expensive, then it must be over a long distance.) Later in the Module, (see "Bridges" in B4), pupils need to determine the relationship between a larger number of variables. Here, they will need to consciously hold some variables constant while they consider relationships between the others.

3. Interpreting intervals and gradients

Most pupils appear to find the interpretation of intervals and gradients difficult and often confuse them with values at particular points. The following two examples both taken from the Problem Collection on pages 193 and 194, illustrate this.

The Motorway Journey

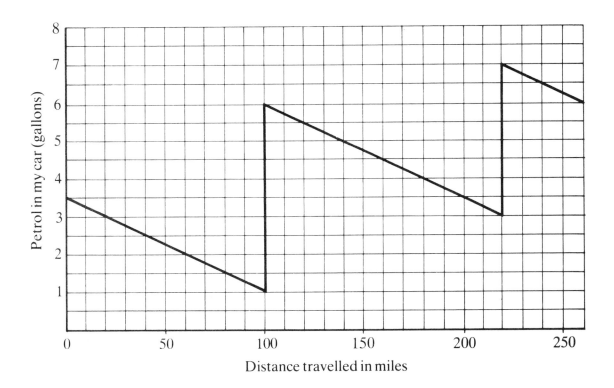

"At which station did I buy the most petrol?"
"At the second because the graph goes higher".

Growth Curves

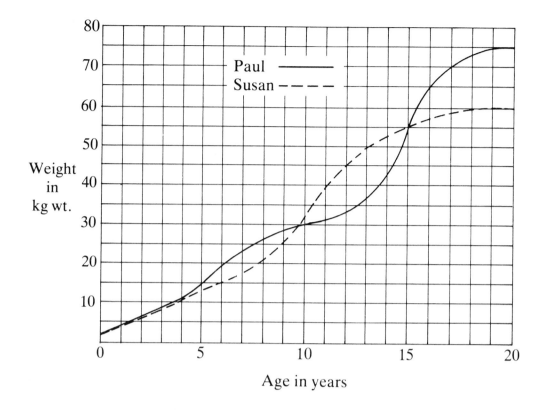

Age in years

"Who was growing faster at the age of 14?"

"Susan, because the Susan's graph is higher when she's 14."

These kinds of response are by no means unusual. Other common errors occur because pupils are unable to compare large segments of a graph although they may be successful with smaller segments. Pupils who interpret graphs in a point-wise fashion are particularly vulnerable to these kinds of error and need to be shown how segments can be compared directly on a graph without having to resort to any kind of scale reading. Often, pupils will measure an interval by 'scale reading', by which we mean that they take two readings and find the arithmetic difference between them. An alternative approach which we term 'grid reading' involves measuring the length of an interval using the grid lines and then using the scale along one axis to decide upon the meaning of this length. When a qualitative comparison of two intervals is to be made this last step is of course unnecessary. Many aspects of graphical interpretation are facilitated by 'grid reading'. It enables pupils to read the graph in a 'relative' way and frees them from the need to keep referring back to the axes and assigning absolute values to every reading that is taken.

For example, in response to the questions "At which station do I buy the most petrol?", a 'scale reader' would reason: "At the first station the graph rises from 1 gallon to 6 gallons, an increase of 5 gallons. At the second station the graph rises from 3 gallons to 7 gallons, an increase of 4 gallons. So more petrol is bought at the first station."

216

However, the 'grid reader' would reason: "The first increase is larger than the second increase, as the vertical line is longer". Grid reading thus has powerful advantages, but from our observations pupils don't always adopt this method successfully and spontaneously.

4. Situations which are not time dependent

Many graphs involve "time" as the independent or as an implicit variable. When this is not the case, however, the function has to be visualised as the outcome of a great number (or infinite number) of experiments. Here are examples of both categories:

'Time dependent'

"Sketch a graph to show the speed of an athlete varies during the course of a 1500 metre race." Although the word 'time' will not appear as one of the labels on the axes (these will be speed and distance covered), one can readily imagine taking measurements of speed and distance at various *times* during a *single* race. Time is thus an implicit variable.

'Time independent'

"Sketch a graph to show how the time for running a race will depend upon the length of the race." Here, we need to imagine that a *large number* of races are performed (in any order), and that the length and time are measured for each race. Each point on the sketch graph will represent a different race, and one cannot imagine time elapsing in the same way as before. In this sense, although the word "Time" appears as a label on the vertical axis, the situation is essentially independent of time.

'Time independent' situations are usually much more difficult to visualise, and often cause pupils considerable difficulty. There are examples of these scattered throughout the module. The first example on Worksheet A3, page 82, is of this type.

3 WAYS OF WORKING IN THE CLASSROOM

Establishing a Framework

There are three major types of activities to manage in the classroom:

i)   Exposition, where the teacher introduces the task to be tackled, explains, sets the scene, organises the structure of the lesson, summarises the results and so on.

ii)   Small group discussion, where pupils work cooperatively, with the teacher available for counselling and discussion when required.

iii) Class discussion, where groups report back to the whole class with the teacher acting as the 'chairperson', or where individual groups discuss together, again with the teacher as 'chairperson'.

Before looking at these activities in detail and the demands they make on the teacher, it is useful to consider the different rhythms that emerge with various tasks and different pupils. Observation of the materials in use shows that the length of time spent working in these different ways varies a great deal. You may care to keep a note of the rhythm of your lessons with different worksheets and different classes and compare them with those obtained by other teachers.

Here is one record from a teacher working with the A5 worksheet, 'Bottles':

Time	Duration	Activities	Comments
11.34	8 mins	Class discussion	Introducing the situation via a problem. (The class is already organised)
11.42	6 mins	Group work	Sketching graphs for cylindrical bottles (page 1)
11.48	8 mins	Class discussion	Group compare sketches.
11.56	18 mins	Group work in pairs	Matching bottles to graphs (pages 2,3)
12.14	7 mins	Class discussion	Groups compare results.
12.21	4 mins	Group work	Sketching graphs for given bottles (page 4)
12.25	5 mins	Class discussion	Groups compare sketches, then homework is set.

In this example, the lesson contained an equal amount of class discussion and small group work, with little or no teacher exposition. (This may be compared with other teachers who preferred a great deal more work in small groups.) What kind of rhythm do you typically adopt?

i)   **Teacher Exposition**

The teacher may at various stages wish to talk to the whole class. If a new concept is to be introduced it will be necessary to explain the new idea perhaps employing a question/answer technique to involve and interest the children. It is important to recognise that this 'teacher-led' part of the lesson is very different from a class discussion, where the teacher acts as chairperson and facilitates communication between the children.

A period of exposition is also often necessary when the teacher is attempting to organise and structure the way in which the children will work. For example, the following flow diagramwas developed with a class during a 'teacher-led' episode at the beginning of worksheet A2, 'Are graphs just pictures?':

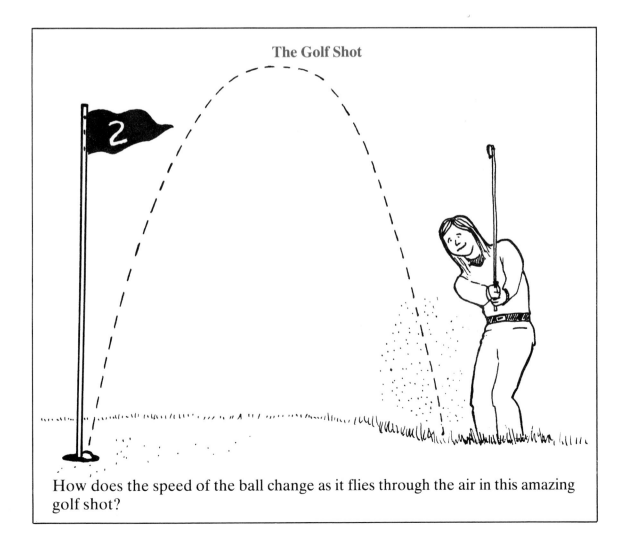

The Golf Shot

How does the speed of the ball change as it flies through the air in this amazing golf shot?

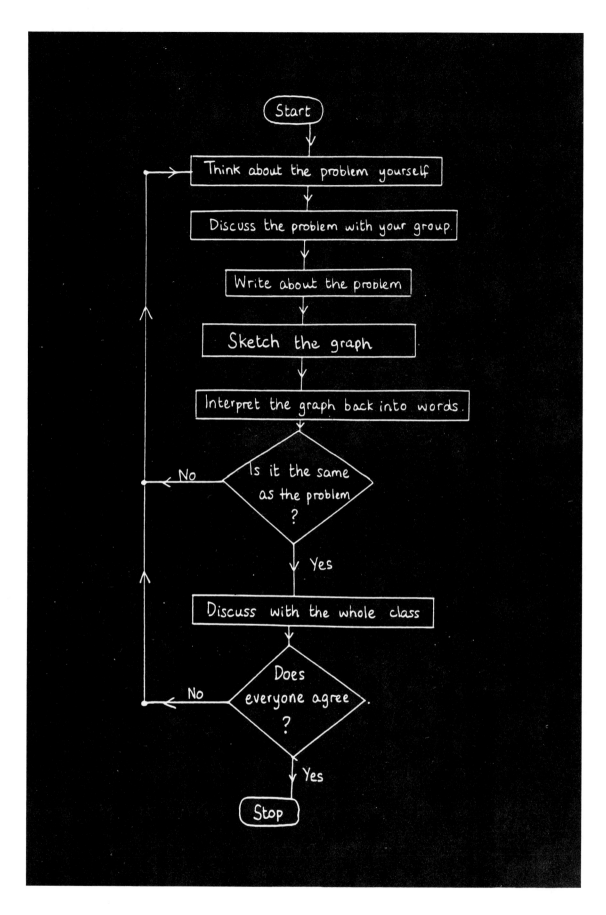

In this lesson, and in several following lessons, the children found that this chart helped them considerably in achieving profitable discussions.

ii) Small group discussion

After the problem has been introduced the children are usually asked to work in pairs or small groups. At the beginning of a new task, it often takes some time to absorb all the information and ideas. The group discussions at the beginning of the task may therefore be fragmentary, using keywords, half sentences, questions and so on. We refer to this as the exploratory discussion stage. Although it often appears somewhat disjointed and poorly articulated, if the group is left to work undisturbed, it is here that organising and reformulation can emerge.

If you are able to tape record some small group discussions you may like to analyse them in the following way*:

---

1. Divide the discussion into a number of distinct episodes or subtopics, as self-contained as possible.

   Identify the initiator of the episode, and discover whether the initiator is a group member or leader (teacher).

---

2. Can you find examples of participants:

   a) putting forward a tentative or hypothetical idea, and asking for comment?
   b) supporting their own assertions with evidence?
   c) contributing evidence in favour of someone else's assertion?
   d) pointing out flaws in the arguments or questioning 'facts' put forward by others?

   Are all members of the group:
   e) participating?
   f) supporting the discussion?

---

3. What kinds of intellectual process were being used? Count the following, putting doubtful cases into more than one category if necessary:

   a) contributions principally at the level of *specific information* (data);
   b) contributions that focus on *ideas* or *concepts* (classes of events, objects or processes);
   c) the number of *abstractions or principles* involving more than one concept.

---

*Categories 1, 2a, b, c, d and 3 are taken from 'Communicating in the Classroom', chapter 4, by Trevor Kerry, edited by Clive Sutton, and published by Hodder and Stoughton, London 1981, ISBN 0 340 26659 7

Below we give a transcript of three boys working on worksheet A1, annotated with these discussion categories:

A1 INTERPRETING POINTS

As you work through this booklet, discuss your answers with your neighbours and try to come to some agreement.

1.   The Bus Stop Queue

Who is represented by each point on the scattergraph, below?

Alice   Brenda   Cathy   Dennis   Errol   Freda

Gavin

Age

1.

2.

3.

4.

5.

6.

7.

Height

1.

<table>
<tr><th colspan="2" align="center">Transcript</th><th colspan="2" align="center">Category and Comment</th></tr>
<tr><td>P1</td><td>Right. Obviously the two highest are Alice and Errol.</td><td>1
3a</td><td>Initiator is P1 not the teacher
Specific information contributed</td></tr>
<tr><td>P2

P1
P2</td><td>Yeah, Numbers 1 and 2 are both the tallest.
Yes.
Therefore they're Alice and Errol.</td><td>2b</td><td>P2 makes an assertion, but it is based on the misconception that 'high points' = 'tall people':</td></tr>
<tr><td>P1

P2</td><td>Hold on! No! 1 and 2 are both the two oldest. They're Errol And Alice.
Yeah. That's what I said.</td><td>2d</td><td>P1 points out a flaw in P2's argument, but then makes a slip himself.</td></tr>
<tr><td>P1</td><td>Sorry . . .I think it could be Dennis and Alice?</td><td>2a</td><td>P1 puts forward a tentative (correct) idea.</td></tr>
<tr><td>P2</td><td>But Dennis is shorter.</td><td>2d</td><td>P2 questions P1's conclusion.</td></tr>
<tr><td>P1

P2</td><td>How do you know that Freda isn't older then?
Don't be silly. Use your common sense.</td><td>2d</td><td>P1 seems to be trying to point out a flaw in P2's argument by questioning.</td></tr>
<tr><td>P1</td><td>Um . . .so Alice'll be the older one. So Alice'll be number 2. OK?</td><td>2a</td><td>P1 returns to his own approach and asks for comment.</td></tr>
<tr><td>P2</td><td>What? She's the oldest and she's the tallest?</td><td>2d</td><td>P2 implies that there is a flaw in P1's argument.</td></tr>
<tr><td>P1

P2</td><td>The other oldest one is short, so that's number 1 isn't it and that's Dennis. Hey up will you two do something?
Well it says agree and I'm agreeing!</td><td>2b

3b

2e

2f</td><td>P1 supports his assertion with evidence.
P1 looks at both variables simultaneously.
P1 feels that he is doing most of the work!
although P3 was silent during the episode, he was supportive and involved.</td></tr>
</table>

You may now like to try analysing the following transcript, which shows how the same three boys tackled page 3 of worksheet A1.

3. Telephone Calls

One weekend,
five people made telephone
calls to various parts of
the country.

They recorded both the cost
of their calls, and the length
of time they were on the
telephone, on the graph below:

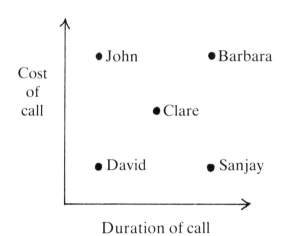

- Who was ringing long-distance? Explain your reasoning carefully.

- Who was making a local call? Again, explain.

- Which people were dialling roughly the same distance? Explain.

- Copy the graph and mark other points which show people making local calls of different durations.

- If you made a similar graph showing every phone call made in Britain during one particular weekend, what would it look like? Draw a sketch, and clearly state any assumptions you make.

3

Transcript	Category and Comment
P1 David and Sanjay were making local calls . . . because they were the cheapest weren't they?	
P2 At the bottom.	
P1 How would you say at the bottom, silly?	
P2 At the bottom of the graph.	
P3 It could be at the bottom of the pond!	
P1 Right. If Barbara was phoning long distance, it would cost far more.	
P2 Oh, yes!	
P3 Yes right. See. If the call is short, it's going to cost that much. If he's doing twice as much it's going to cost two times as much.	
P2 Yeah, right.	
P3 The longer you're on the phone, the more it costs.	
P2 I don't think duration means distance.	
P1 No, it means length of time.	
P3 Oh, John and Barbara have actually had the most expensive calls together, but John . . . but John was ringing long distance.	
P2 Yes, but you've got to explain it.	
P1 John was phoning long distance because his call was shortest and cost the most. David was making the local call . . .	
P3 No, it was Sanjay who was making the local call.	
P2 How can it be Sanjay?	
P1 Because he spoke for a long time and it's still very cheap.	
P2 Oh. Makes sense . . . unusually!	

The three pupils appear to have become involved and interested in these tasks, and they feel confident enough within their group to offer opinions and suggestions. (It is interesting to note here that Pupil 3 was joining in the discussion by the time the group got to the telephone problem.)

When children are working in pairs or in groups the balance of communication is extremely sensitive to teacher intervention. When an 'audience' is present, the group may try to supply 'answers' for the teacher rather than reasoned arguments to convince the 'group'. The teacher is also an *informed* audience who, most children assume, knows and understands the work. Some may therefore see no need to persuade the teacher in a reasoned way because "teacher knows what I mean". Others, however, may decide to present their arguments more formally because of the presence of an authoritative figure. During a full class discussion, and, to a lesser extent, during a small group discussion with the teacher present, there may be a shift towards the 'distant audience' mode as defined in the tables below:*

	Intimate Audience	Distant Audience
Size	Small group	Full class
Source of authority	The group	The teacher
Relationships	Intimate.............	Public
Ordering of thought	Inexplicit	Explicit
Speech planning	Improvised.........	Pre-planned
Speech function	Exploratory	Final draft

As the nature of the audience has such a profound effect on children's thought processes, the teacher should be careful of the timing and frequency of such 'interventions' or 'interruptions'. Eventually a group will be ready to offer its ideas to the whole class, but it will first need time and space to work out its own ideas within the group.

*'From Communication to Curriculum', Douglas Barnes, published by Penguin 1976. ISBN 0 14 080382 3

(iii) Class Discussion

A checklist is given on the inside back cover of this book, headed 'Classroom Discussion Checklist'. It provides some general guidance both for the running of full class discussions and for encouraging small group discussions.

This table is not intended to show that 'judging' or 'evaluating' a pupil's response is always inappropriate, it rather attempts to recognise that if the teacher operates in this way, then the nature of the discussion will change, either into a period of teacher-led exposition or into a rather inhibited period of 'answer guessing' where the emphasis is on externally acceptable performances rather than on exploratory dialogue. Typically, therefore, if judgements are to be made, then they should be made towards the end of a discussion.

Barnes* using two categories to describe distinct teaching styles which he terms 'Reply' and 'Assess':

> "When a teacher *replies* to his pupils he is by implication taking their view of the subject seriously, even though he may wish to extend and modify it. This strengthens the learner's confidence in actively interpreting the subject-matter; teacher and learner are in a collaborative relationship. When a teacher *assesses* what his pupils say he distances himself from their views, and allies himself with external standards which may implicitly devalue what the learner himself has constructed. Both reply and assess are essential parts of teaching; *assessment* is turned towards the public standards against which pupils must eventually measure themselves, whereas *reply* is turned towards the pupils as he is, and towards his own attempts, however primitive, to make sense of the world.
>
> If a teacher stresses the assessment function at the expense of the reply function, this will urge his pupils towards externally acceptable performances, rather than towards trying to relate new knowledge to old. In this case, the externals of communication— accepted procedures, the vocabulary and style of the subject, even the standard lay-out for writing—are likely to be given more weight than the learner's attempts to formulate meaning. A classroom dialogue in which sharing predominates over presenting, in which the teacher replies rather than assesses, encourages pupils when they talk and write to bring out existing knowledge to be reshaped by new points of view being presented to them. This is likely to be difficult for teacher and pupil alike."

The presentation of group ideas to the whole class can be organised in various ways. (This is raised as Discussion Pause 2 on the videotape.) Very often it becomes a teacher-led discussion. Adelman, Elliot et al** offer the following hypotheses about teacher-led discussions — they are well worth considering:

---

*   'From Communication to Curriculum', Douglas Barnes, Penguin 1976.
** 'Implementing the Principles of Inquiry/Discovery Teaching: Some Hypotheses', Adelman C., Elliot J. et al, Centre for Applied Research in Education, University of East Anglia, 1974.

227

1 Asking many questions of pupils...may raise too many of the teacher's own ideas and leave no room for those of the pupil. Responding to pupils' questions with many ideas may stifle the expression of their own ideas.

2 Re-formulating problems in the teacher's own words may prevent pupils from clarifying them for themselves.

3 When the teacher changes the direction of enquiry or point of discussion, pupils may fail to contribute their own ideas. They will interpret such actions as attempts to get them to conform with his own line of reasoning.

4 When the teacher always asks a question following a pupil's response to his previous question, he may prevent pupils from introducing their own ideas.

5 When the teacher responds to pupils' ideas with utterances like 'good', 'yes', 'right', 'interesting', etc., he may prevent others from expressing alternative ideas. Such utterances may be interpreted as rewards for providing the responses required by the teacher.

Asking children to present work or explain ideas to the whole class needs very sensitive handling. It is essential to try to create an atmosphere in which errors and poorly expressed ideas are welcomed and discussed rather than criticised and ridiculed. Attempts to achieve this kind of atmosphere can take on many practical forms. For example, the teacher may:

— collect in a few suggestions from pupils, write them on the blackboard and discuss them anonymously — thus avoiding any embarrassment.
— ask a representative from each group to describe the consensus view obtained by their *group*. Solutions thus become associated with groups rather than with individuals.

It is also possible to rearrange the desks or tables (in a U shape, for example) so that it becomes clear that the activity is discussion rather than exposition. Once the right atmosphere is established, most pupils seem to enjoy and benefit from taking part in an orderly, well managed class discussion.

What do the children think?

The following transcript is the final part of an interview where children were asked to discuss their experiences of class discussion with this module. (There were 9 pupils from a 4th year O-level group — each pupil was chosen by his or her coworkers to represent their views.)

(I = interviewer, P = one pupil, PP = two pupils, etc)

PP   Yes it was good ... it worked well in the class.

P   It's good to have discussion.

P   I think we don't normally do any discussion with the groups ... that brought a change.

P   I'd like more discussion in the maths lessons.

P   It was good the way ... Mr T was a bit false with it 'cos he went round talking to people and normally he just sits at the desk and marks people's work ... but you were discussing it in your groups ...and then maybe 10 minutes at the end of the lesson discussing the questions as a class and the people would put their points forward.

P   Yes.

I   What about the class discussion bit then ... was it good or bad?

PP   Good, good.

I   OK let's take it through ... what makes a good class discussion then?

P   Well you're not having everyone shouting out at the same time ... and you listen to other people's ideas ... then you put yours ...

I   Did that happen?

PP   Yes, yes.

P   You get people to come forward and like draw their ideas on the blackboard and then people can criticise it and comment on it ... and like you say ... you're in your little groups maybe 3 or 4 ideas put forward and eventually decide on one and in a class maybe 7 or 8 ideas put forward and then you can ...yours might be right and you stick with it ...

I   So the class discussion enables one group to compare their results with another group.

PPP   Yes, yes.

I   There were times when Mr T started the lesson off, for example, with an introduction ... was that useful?

PP   Yes, yes it reminded you.

I   So it was helpful?

P   I think you should start discussing it yourself; then have 10-15 minutes at the end of the lesson to draw the ideas together ...

PP   Yes, yes.

P   When you get into the lesson you don't really want to sit down and listen to somebody at the front talking on a unit . . . you want to get down to some work, then discuss it.

P   'Cos then you can make mistakes . . . and learn from your mistakes, can't you?

I   So from the point of view of the lessons you would have rather had a brief start from the teacher, work on your own or in your group and then a 10 minute discussion at the end.

PP   Yes, yes.

P   'Cos Mr T goes on a bit when he starts talking! You can't stop him!

I   So you found that not so good then?

P   Yes he went on for too long when he's talking.

I   OK that's part of life . . . every teacher's different, you have to cope with teachers don't you . . .

P   He's a good teacher, but he goes on!

I   OK . . . so if we were putting down notes for a teacher you'd recommend the short start and so on . . .

PP   Yes.

I   Are there any other things that you would say or recommend?

P   I think it was good . . . you don't need much knowledge . . . I think you need experience really and what you do is . . . you relate your experiences you see and that I think develops your intelligence more than just knowledge.

P   Yes . . . if you're not very clever then . . . people can take it as far as they want . . . if you enjoy the questions you can go all over. You can draw graphs and compare with other people's, but if you're not so interested you can just draw one graph, say "I think that's right" and go on to the next question.

These children appear to have enjoyed this way of working. The last part of the videotape shows another group of children discussing their views on the classroom activities.

4 HOW CAN THE MICRO HELP?

The resource pack with this Module book contains four microcomputer programs: SUNFLOWER, BRIDGES, BOTTLES and TRAFFIC. The SUNFLOWER program and the BRIDGES program may be considered together. Below, we give a brief description of each. (Fuller documentation is provided in the accompanying handbook.)

SUNFLOWER

SUNFLOWER is a problem solving exercise which encourages systematic investigation and modelling. You are challenged to grow the world's tallest sunflower. You have three unlabelled jars containing chemicals which you can add in any quantity to the plant's water. The program introduces ideas about scientific method and practises place value in the use of decimals.

Pupil Activities: observing, exploring, experimenting, interpreting, modelling.

BRIDGES

BRIDGES allows you to specify the length, width and thickness of a plank which is used to make a bridge. Once the bridge dimensions are defined, the program provides the maximum weight that the bridge can support before collapsing. Simple animation as well as numerical data is shown.

Pupil Activities: exploring, generalising, problem solving.

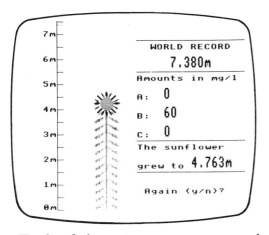

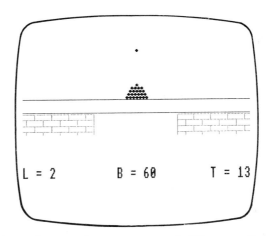

Each of these two programs may be viewed as a 'data generator'. The pupils are invited to choose values for the independent variables (the quantities of chemicals administered to the sunflower, or the dimensions of the bridge); the computer then performs an 'experiment' and gives the resulting value of the dependent variable (the height to which the sunflower grows, or the maximum weight the bridge will support). With SUNFLOWER, the objective is to maximise the height of the sunflower that can be grown, whereas with BRIDGES the objective is to discover an underlying 'law' by which the strength of any bridge may be predicted. The BRIDGES program is therefore suitable for older, more able pupils, while SUNFLOWER can be used with pupils of more limited ability (where it will also provide considerable practice in using decimal place value). SUNFLOWER provides a very suitable introduction to BRIDGES.

Naturally, these programs are both simplified models of reality, but they provide a powerful way of 'setting the scene' (using cartoon graphics) and by performing the technical tasks involved in data generation, they allow pupils to focus on fundamental processes of scientific inquiry: exploring systematically (holding some variables constant while exploring relationships between the others, etc), creating graphs and tables, looking for patterns and making generalisations.

The BOTTLES and TRAFFIC programs may also be considered together:

BOTTLES

BOTTLES encourages pupils to explore the relationship between graphs and events in a realistic context. Animated graphics show a bottle filling steadily with water while a graph shows how the height of liquid varies as the volume in the bottle increases. How does the graph change when the bottle changes in shape or size? Can you work out the shape of the bottle when you only have the graph?

Pupil Activities: observing, discussing, graph interpretation, graph sketching.

TRAFFIC

TRAFFIC develops graph interpretation skills by using animated graphics to help pupils' understanding of distance-time graphs, and by challenging them to match graphs with realistic situations. The program begins by asking you to imagine a man in a helicopter who photographs the road below him every few seconds. When his photographs are pinned up in a row, we get a crude distance-time graph of the traffic. How does the movement of vehicles on the road affect the graph? Can you guess what was happening on the road from the graph?

Pupil Activities: observing, discussing, graph interpretation, graph drawing, sketching.

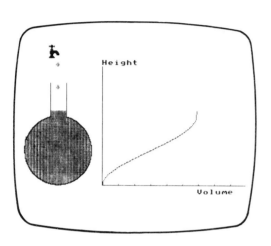

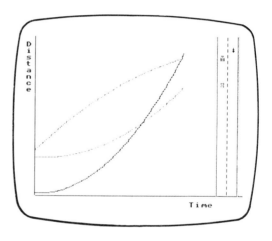

These programs provide two contexts within which pupils can develop their skills at translating pictures into graphs and graphs into pictures. Again, these are described more fully in the accompanying handbooks. Both programs contain a bank of examples which the teacher or pupil can draw on during class, large group or small group discussions. The programs can generate tasks in several ways. It is possible to show just the animations and ask the pupils to sketch the corresponding graphs or vice versa. This flexibility to control a program so that it *leaves out* the activity that the pupils should do themselves, we usually refer to as 'omission design'. (After pupils have sketched their graphs, the computer animation can be replayed with the graph facility switched on, so that pupils can detect errors and misunderstandings in their work.)

Another important idea emerges through the use of these two programs. Sometimes, the computer may be switched off and the children instructed to imitate the same activity in pairs. One pupil writes a story and draws the corresponding graph then passes this graph to her neighbour. The second pupil now has to try to recreate the original story. When the two stories are compared, a great deal of useful discussion is often generated. (Such *role* imitation offers much more than traditional *rule* imitation!)

232

To conclude, the computer can be used in many ways, for example:

— with a whole class it can be used to introduce and explain tasks and provide data or problems for discussion. The teacher can then take on the role of a 'counsellor' or 'fellow pupil', discussing strategies and approaches *with* the children. (This is made much easier if the computer, rather than the teacher, appears to be setting the tasks).

— with a small group of children, it can be used as a 'resource' to be called upon, giving feedback or information when needed. The unthreatening 'personality' of the machine enables it to be treated almost as a member of the group. (If only one computer is available, groups could take turns at using the micro while others work on related worksheets.)

5   ASSESSING THE EXAMINATION QUESTIONS

The examination questions aim to assess and give credit for the following processes:

1. Interpreting mathematical representations using words or pictures.
2. Translating words or pictures into mathematical representations.
3. Translating between mathematical representations.
4. Describing functional relationships using words or pictures.
5. Combining information presented in various ways, and drawing inferences where appropriate.
6. Using mathematical representations to solve problems arising from realistic situations.
7. Describing or explaining the methods used and the results obtained.

The headings above all describe processes outlined in the Module. Each problem will involve at least one of these processes and may involve as many as five. For example, in "The Vending Machine" (page 38) the candidate is required to translate from words to a mathematical representation (Process number 2), while "The Journey" (page 12) involves the processes of interpreting mathematical representations using words, combining information and drawing inferences and, in part (ii), translating into and between mathematical representations (Process numbers 1, 5, 2 and 3).

This section offers a set of activities designed to clarify what is meant by these assessment objectives which obviously cover a broader range than the usual 'method' and 'accuracy' headings used in assessing mathematical technique. These activities aim to help teachers both in understanding better the questions and marking schemes their pupils will face and in assessing informally their work in the classroom.

A marking activity for you to try

1) Consider the questions "Camping" (page 20), "Going to school" (page 28) and "The hurdles race" (page 42) and try to decide which process is being tested at each stage of the problems. Then fill in the following table:

		Process being tested						
		(1)	(2)	(3)	(4)	(5)	(6)	(7)
Camping	(i)							
	(ii)							
	(iii)							
	(iv)							
	(v)							
	(vi)							
Going to school	(i)							
	(ii)							
	(iii)							
	(iv)							
The hurdles race								

This activity is often a useful strategy for starting to devise a mark scheme.

2) Now consider the "Camping" problem. Decide how many marks should be allocated to each part. (There are 15 marks available for this question altogether.) Discuss this with your colleagues. Do you disagree on the weighting of each part? Try to resolve any discrepancies. Do the same for "Going to school", (which is also worth 15 marks).

You may like to compare your allocation with those we gave. The marking schemes for these two questions are given on pages 21 and 30. They also show the more detailed allocation of the marks within the sections.

If you have enough time, you may like to look at the pupils' responses provided for these two questions in the 'Specimen Examination Questions' section. Try to mark them using your marking schemes.

3) Since a marking scheme for "The hurdles race" is more difficult to devise we suggest that you devote the remainder of the marking session to this problem. The above strategy is not applicable to this question. Pupil responses can be extremely varied. If you haven't already done so, answer the problem yourself and then discuss which points you consider to be important for the candidate to mention. Make a list. It may be quite long — and there only 8 marks available for this question, so try to decide which factors you consider to be of greater importance.

Below, six scripts from candidates are provided for this question. (They are also contained within the 'Masters for Photocopying'.) Read them all through once before trying to assess them. On the basis of your overall impression, rank them in order with the best first. (Do not discuss this rank ordering with your colleagues yet.) Record your rank orders in column R_0 of the Marking Record Form.

Marking Record Form

Script	Marker 1				Marker 2				Marker 3				Marker 4			
	R_0	R_1	M_1	M_2	R_0	R_1	M_1	M_2	R_0	R_1	M_1	M_2	R_0	R_1	M_1	M_2
A Sharon																
B Sean																
C Simon																
D David																
E Jackie																
F Nicola																

Key:
Impression rank order R_0
Raw mark M_1
Mark rank order R_1
Revised mark (if any) M_2

Next, compare the list of the factors that you consider important with the lists obtained by your colleagues and with our mark scheme on page 43. Discuss any discrepancies.

Use our mark scheme to mark the 6 scripts and record your marks in column M_1. Record also the new rank order implied from your marking in the preceding column, R_1.

Now compare your result with your colleagues', considering each of the 6 scripts in turn. Try to account for any differences that occur and enter any revised marks in column M_2 of the Marking Record Form.

Finally you may like to compare your assessments with those we have made, on page 240.

Script A   Sharon

Competitor (A) starts off with a good pace and is getting faster and starts to slow alittle at the end but not drasticly.
Competitor (B) is making a good pace but he isn't going as fast as (A) about half way in the race. Right near the end he decides to quicken up his pace. He is taking more time to do the race
Competitor (C) starts off with a really fast run but he tires himself out and has to keep himself as the same pace for awhile. I think he's stopped he's not making any mileage at all but he stops running again. But he has taken the most time.

Script B   Sean

In the first seconds of the race C made
the best start followed by A and B bringing up the rear
but after a few seconds C has hit a hurdle and fallen
which leaves A in the lead followed by B. Once C has
got up again he starts once more but cannot catch up.
In the later stages of the race A is beginning to tire
and B is putting on a final burst of acceleration to
reach the tape first followed closely by A
and C came last.

Script C   Simon

HURDLES RACE.

2 C gets out of the blocks first
followed by A then b. Oh tragedy
C has fallen at about 120 m. So
A is in the lead coming up to
the finish followed by b then C.
Oh and b is putting up a late
challenge and the result is 1st B
2nd A 3rd C

Script D   David

They're off   All going well   As they come up to the
hundrend metre mark B leads from A   with C behind
Oh no C has hit the hurdle badly   but yes he's alright
and they're he's up again.
Approaching the 200 metre mark   A has overtaken B
C is still lagging behind badley.
At 300 metres its still A from B. C is out
of the race because he so far behind.
A is tiring, Yes B has over-taken A   At the
line its B then A   with C still hobbeling
round the track.

Script E   Jackie

Athlete A on the first 100m is in second place when he has past the 100m mark the time is about 10 seconds. His speed stays about the same through the next 100m and as he passes 300m mark the time is about 50 seconds
He finishes the race in about 1minute 10 seconds.

Athlete B on the first 100m is slower on the first 100m than Athlete A his time after 100m is about 20 seconds. His speed stays about the same through the next 100m and as he passes the 300m mark the time is about 60 seconds.
He finishes the race in about 1minute 5 seconds so he quickened up near the end.

Athlete C is quicker than Athlete A, B in the first 100m at about the 150 metre mark he ~~goes~~ stops gradually but quickens up again on the last 200m but he finishes the race in about 1minute 40 seconds.

Script F   Nicola

No C ~~go~~ runs fast at the beginning with A a bit slower & B the slowest of all. A then picks up speed and B is going almost as fast, but C now slows down quite a lot. A & B are side by side as they near the end of the race but B wins, just by a few seconds. C is third, quite a while after A.

Suggested mark scheme applied to the six scripts:

		Script					
		A	B	C	D	E	F
1 mark for each of these.	At start, C takes lead		1	1		1	1
	After a while, C stops	1	1	1	1	1	
	Near end, B overtakes A		1	1	1		1
	B wins		1	1	1		1
2 marks for 4 of these, or 1 mark for 2 of these	A and B pass C		√	√			
	C starts running again		√		√	√	
	C runs at slower pace				√		
	A slows down *or* B speeds up	√	√	√	√	√	
	A is second *or* C is last		√	√	√		√
Quality of commentary		0	2	1	2	0	1
TOTAL		1	8	6	7	3	4